Health
and Social Problems
in the School

Health Education,
Physical Education, and
Recreation Series

RUTH ABERNATHY, Ph.D., EDITORIAL ADVISER

Chairman, Department for Women,
School of Physical and Health Education,
University of Washington, Seattle, Washington,
98105

Health
and Social Problems
in the School

(Case Studies for School Personnel)

MORRIS HAMBURG, ED.D.
Associate Professor of Education,
Brooklyn College, New York

and

MARIAN V. HAMBURG, ED.D.
Associate Professor,
and Director of Health Education,
New York University School of Education,
New York

Foreword by   *Richard L. Foster*

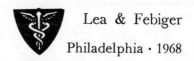
Lea & Febiger
Philadelphia · 1968

Foreword

During the last decade, the major thrusts in American education have been toward the cognitive areas... the basic skills, the sciences, the mathematics, and the disciplines. A major concern with the humanities and with health education, other than the physical fitness area, has been lost in this milieu. The program for health education has been neglected in teacher education and even more neglected in the public schools. The result could be a highly educated man but one with little understanding of himself or his feelings.

The Hamburgs, in their case study approach, have introduced a unique way for both teacher education and for elementary and secondary schools to use viable material for the development of basic principles, not only in health education but of sound management in relationship to health education. As a practicing superintendent, reading the case studies, I realized that I had lived through many such studies, had heard the same responses from community members, and anticipated many of the replies made by members of the Boards of Trustees. The mention of alcohol, narcotics, smoking, or sex seems to be able to bring out unusual reactions from people, rather than evoking an inquiry approach into the fundamental causes of aberrant behavior. Moral decisions tend to be made, rather than analytical and constructive proposals being advanced. The fact that the authors decided not to reach conclusions in any of their studies but to leave each study open for discussion is one of the promising parts of their work. Students analyzing these cases should be better able to prepare themselves to face the over-responses that they will encounter, either as health educators or as administrators. It would also seem to me that students should have the opportunity to see the cases as personal and dynamic. Students could become extremely inner-active with the material.

In this book the Hamburgs deal with the insights that they have gathered from many years of work, both in health education and in the schools. They have made a contribution with the model that they are using, and it should serve as a newer and richer approach to health education. It can be said with a great deal of confidence that the material will affect the concepts, the attitudes, and the behaviors of those who are deeply involved with health education.

Danville, California   RICHARD L. FOSTER
                                      District Superintendent
                                      San Ramon District
                                      Valley Unified School

Preface

This is a collection of cases — happenings, if you will, each based on a perplexing situation that actually occurred in a school system somewhere in the United States. Each one describes how personnel really functioned in approaching a resolution of the problem affecting the physical and emotional health of youth.

The book was written because of the need for practical "situational" material dealing with current health and social problems which confront school personnel. There is adequate literature of a philosophical and theoretical nature to provide a cognitive foundation for the school's role. But there is little case study material to provide the basis for discussion of the application of principles to real problems. We intend for this book to provide a means by which the theory relating to the conduct of the school health program can be applied to practice.

Solutions to the cases are purposely omitted. There is a wide variety of possibilities for each case, and these will vary with individual perception of the problems and the means for their most satisfactory handling. The fact is that there are no perfect answers to the questions posed — fundamental questions, such as: Who shall teach health? Should it be required? How shall controversial topics like sex education be handled? How should schools deal with pressure groups? How many services can (should) a school provide? Can (should) student smoking in schools be eliminated? What physical education for handicapped children? How confidental are health records? How can the growing use of drugs be curbed? Alcohol education — is it realistic?

These and numerous other old and new questions require serious consideration by all school personnel. One can pinpoint who in the schools is responsible for mathematics — or social studies — or music. In fact, almost any course of study and most school services are identified with specific personnel. But health and social problems are not easily designated as the province of a single department or specialist. There exists not only a wide range of opinion on the nature, extent and scope of the school health services and curricula, but also confusion about who assumes the major responsibilities. Health and social problems of school age children appear to be everybody's business.

These cases are intended for use in teacher training programs for elementary classroom teachers, secondary teachers (particularly those specializing in health education), school nurses, guidance counselors and school administrators. The cases should be equally useful as the basis for school district in-service education programs. Further, the cases should commend themselves as the practical content for workshops and seminars for those administrators who believe that more than lip service must be given to the school health program and pupil personnel services.

The use of cases as an instructional technique needs no defense. The literature abounds with data supporting this teaching technique in practically all disciplines. However, there is often confusion between critical incidents and case studies. Cases should provide data about the educational issues as well as about the personalities involved. This permits the consideration of those human factors that so often determine the resolution of the issue. These cases, based on actual situations in schools, have been tested in graduate classes and found to be good catalysts for depth analysis of theory applied to practice.

Like any other teaching method, a single approach can be overdone. Case studies allow for a variety of presentations. Group discussion is perhaps the most familiar way to use cases. But they are equally effective when discussed by a panel, and become more dramatic when several people actually play the roles. The conversational style in which these cases are written allows personalities to emerge, and makes it possible for "characters" to project their convictions about the solution to the problem. Several "casts" acting out solutions to the same case can reveal a variety of "endings"

Procedures will depend upon the composition, needs and sophistication of the group involved. Whatever approach is used, experience has shown that it is necessary to provide sufficient opportunity for discussants to become thoroughly familiar with the case in advance. Then it is important to allow at least two hours for its discussion and analysis. The skill of the leader in remaining neutral will enhance the discussion. The cases are also suitable for written analysis, and they are particularly valuable for providing a basis for correlating theory and practice. They have been used successfully as a testing device.

The cases have been organized on the pattern of Suggested School Health Policies, a publication of the Joint Committee on Health Problems in Education of the National Education Association and the American Medical Association, a source which provides guidance in the discussion of all of the cases.

The extensive reference lists, specific to the health and social problems highlighted in the cases and to the related administrative theory, are intended to provide a rich source of professional thinking on all aspects of the cases.

We wish to acknowledge the assistance of the many school personnel throughout the country who helped in collecting data for the cases — among these are Ellen

Norman, Reda Williams, Doris Terry, Helen Woods, Kenneth Briney, Mildred Doster and Odell Jack. We are also indebted to those graduate students at New York University and Brooklyn College who sparked some of the ideas for cases and who also served as guinea pigs for testing their value in group discussion. We also appreciate the aid of our daughter, Jackie, who helped to type the manuscript.

New York, N.Y.   MORRIS HAMBURG
                                    MARIAN V. HAMBURG

Contents

Qualifications of School Health Personnel

School Health Education

1

Where In Health
Are We Going?

A Senior honor student requests an excuse from required Physical Education and Health in order to participate in the school's marching band.

"GOOD morning, Barbara. Sit down for a minute while I try to clear some of this mess off my desk. The first day of school always brings its problems, and it's hard to think clearly with so many papers in front of me. O.K., that's better," said the guidance counselor, as he put some of the papers into a desk drawer. "Now, what can I do for you?"

"Well, I really do have a problem, Mr. Gillespie," Barbara Martin began. "It's about my program for this semester. When we talked about my schedule last spring and you told me that I would have to take Health this fall, I suppose I was rather silly to put it off until my senior year, but something always came up that made it inconvenient. And now I've been scheduled to take Phys Ed and Health during a ninth period. Is this something new?"

"Well, yes it is," Mr. Gillespie responded. "Jefferson is really bursting out at the seams this year. We have about 150 more freshmen than last year and there just isn't enough room to accommodate all of our scheduled classes, so we just had to find some way to stretch the day. We were tightly scheduled as it was with our normal eight-period day, but this additional influx of students was the straw that broke the camel's back. So this year we have a staggered schedule of ten periods, including lunch and study halls. All juniors and seniors are scheduled for periods one through eight, and our freshmen and sophomores will be in session for periods three through ten. That gives us a little more time to stagger the schedules so that we can handle the numbers. I know this sounds complicated, but believe me, Barbara, it's the only way we can take care of the situation."

"I know we didn't have a ninth period last year," the girl said, "and that's why I didn't know what to think when I saw my schedule with Gym in the ninth. But if the juniors and seniors finish their school day at the end of the eighth period, why am I scheduled for a ninth period?"

"Let me look at your schedule again, Barbara. I remember that it was a most difficult one." Mr. Gillespie looked at her card and then said, "Oh, now I remember. To begin with, your four solid subjects are fixed because you are in the honors section, and there is only one of each of these offered. This includes Advanced Placement Chemistry with 5 labs per week. So they can't be changed. Then you were given permission to take the Typing class being offered to academic seniors and also Driver Education. Those courses are fixed too. With this schedule there is no time other than the ninth period that you could possibly take the Physical Education and Health. You'll have to take that with the freshmen and sophomores, but even so, you're lucky we didn't have to put it into the tenth period!"

"Oh, now I'm beginning to understand," the girl said as she pondered, "but I don't see how I can do it."

"I think you can. Your record is so good. If you weren't an honor student, you wouldn't even be permitted to have such a full schedule, but your grades warrant it, and I have every confidence that you will come through with flying colors as usual. Anyway, what's so bad about the ninth period? It will be your last class of the day, and at least you'll have enough time to get into your street clothes after gym without rushing."

"It's not that I object to the ninth period," Barbara replied. "I think you have forgotten that I've simply *got* to practice with the marching band, and they still begin at the end of the eighth period. Mr. Albinski has made me one of the key people in the new formations for this year, and with the big State competition coming up, he told me that I just have to be there at the beginning of the practices. We have practices every day except Friday, at least until we have our routines perfected. And that's the very time I'm scheduled for Physical Education and Health. I've just got to do something."

"Well, let me see," Mr. Gillespie said. "We have had similar types of special situations before and we've always been able to work out something. Coach Leo, who headed up the Physical Education Department, was always most cooperative in giving permission to substitute participation in the marching band for Physical Education. I don't believe that our new Department Chairman will have any objection. You're scheduled to take Physical Education with freshmen and sophomores on Tuesdays and Thursdays anyhow, and I don't believe you will be missing much by getting your exercise with the band on the football field."

"But what about Health, Mr. Gillespie?"

"As for that, you'll only miss the Monday and Wednesday sessions for a while. At least, you'll be able to get to the Friday class every week. There's no reason why you can't get the reading assignments from your teacher, so you can keep up with the rest of the class until you begin attending class regularly after Thanksgiving. There is no grade in Health anyway. It's just pass or fail. We just offer it because it is a requirement for graduation. Which teacher do you have for Physical Education and Health?"

"Her name is Mrs. Dailey," Barbara replied. "I believe she's new here."

"Oh, yes," Mr. Gillespie said, "she is replacing Miss Carman. I'll give you a note which you can give to her when you meet her class the first time tomorrow. I'm sure you won't have any trouble. And you'd better lead those formations well, because I'll be watching for you at the first home football game."

Two days later Mr. Gillespie welcomed Mrs. Ellen Dailey and her Department Chairman, Gregory Coleman, into his office. Earlier in the day they had requested an appointment.

"I'm Don Gillespie, Chairman of the Guidance Department, Mrs. Dailey. I don't believe I've had the pleasure of meeting you. Welcome to Jefferson High School! And before we proceed further, let me congratulate you, Greg, on your promotion. I never thought Bob Leo would really retire, but evidently he liked the fishing too much this summer, and decided not to come back. He's been threatening to do this every year for the past ten. This time he meant it. I must say I envy him."

"So do I, in a way," said Mr. Coleman.

Turning to Mrs. Dailey, the guidance counselor said, "I hope you will like it here. Have you taught before?"

"I've been in a surburban Chicago school district for the past five years. My husband's company transferred him here quite suddenly this summer, and fortunately for me, Jefferson needed a new teacher. I know I will enjoy working with Mr. Coleman and the rest of you."

"Well, if there is anyway I can help, just let me know," Mr. Gillespie replied. "Now what can I do for you two?"

"Don," Gregory Coleman replied, "we're here to talk about Barbara Martin's request to be excused from Physical Education and two periods of Health until the football season is over. Mrs. Dailey showed me the note you gave to Barbara asking for such an arrangement.

I think you should know that neither one of us is happy about this."

"Why, what do you mean, Greg? I didn't request that she be allowed to drop the course. I merely asked if it would be possible to substitute Marching Band for the P.E. activity period on Tuesdays and Thursdays, and that she be excused for the two periods of Hygiene that meet on Mondays and Wednesdays. She can be in the Health class every Friday, and she fully expects to complete all the assignments that the others do, and to take the same tests. Then, by December first, the marching band practices will be over and she'll attend class regularly on Mondays, Wednesdays and Fridays. Barbara isn't trying to get out of anything. I've known her for the two years she's been here and she is one of our outstanding students. Her program is completely filled and there just isn't any way to schedule it. She doesn't want to take Phys Ed and Health with the underclassmen, but she just has to."

"Why is the marching band so important to her?" Mrs. Dailey asked.

"Well, Barbara is one of the people who make that band click. You haven't seen them perform yet, Mrs. Dailey, but when you do, I think you'll be impressed. They were in 2nd place at the last State competition, and they are hoping to be the winners this year. I can't begin to tell you what the boss thinks about the public relations value of this. I don't really think she should be pulled out of the marching band. She's badly needed there. As a matter of fact, I checked with Albinski and he told me that everything depends upon Barbara being present during practices. We were always able to work out this sort of thing with Coach Leo and there was never any objection. And this is a very special case with Barbara Martin who is an outstanding honor student."

"I must say I thought there must be some mistake

when I saw the note," Mrs. Dailey said. "When I was interviewed during the summer, I was led to believe that the Physical Education and Health classes were looked upon as being an integral part of the school program. That's the way it was at my last school too, and I would like to believe that all subjects are considered to be equally important, especially courses that are required by the State Education Department such as Health and Physical Education. I would hate to think that any students did not get full benefit of the program, which, incidentally, I consider to be minimal."

"But I'm not asking you to excuse Barbara from the course requirements," Mr. Gillespie countered. "After all, she will get plenty of exercise with the marching band on Tuesdays and Thursdays and that ought to substitute for the Gym. As for the Health, she will be there every Friday, and I see no reason why she can't do the reading assignments on her own. You can give her the same tests that you give the rest. The girl is an excellent student and I'll bet she had no trouble in keeping up with the others. As a matter of fact, you can give her extra assignments, if that would make you feel any better."

"I'm afraid you miss the point," Gregory Coleman interjected. "Physical Education and Health requirements are as important as any others, and I think it is time that we recognize this at Jefferson High. I know that Coach Leo had a different point of view. He was mainly interested in his athletes, and I believe his attitude downgraded the Physical Education and Health program. To be specific, I don't believe that Physical Education is merely a means of getting so much exercise per week, as you seem to imply by substituting marching. Our program stresses the importance of developing healthy attitudes toward physical activity throughout life, and should provide our students with lifetime sports skills so that they will be more likely to make exercise a regular part of their lives. It's important, not only as leisure activity that is enjoyable, but actually in prolonging life and helping to prevent some diseases — heart disease, for instance."

"And I would like to say something about the Health Education course," Mrs. Dailey chimed in. "I don't know how the course has been presented until now, but my plans depend upon the active participation of the students. You see, we don't have that old-fashioned 'blood and bones' type of Hygiene, where students were expected to learn the names of the parts of the body and be able to identify them later on tests. Our course content is built on the *real* problems of young adults — things that will make a difference as they become adults. As you can imagine, we study the areas of mental health and social adjustment. We try to help young people understand themselves and their dates, their employers, everybody! And we go in depth into social issues that are appearing almost daily in the newspapers — narcotics, smoking, drug abuse, alcoholism, venereal disease, sex education. These topics are the kinds that must be discussed. There is nothing to memorize, but there is an awful lot to understand. And understanding comes through comparing points of view with others. The student has to *be* there to be able to do that."

"Oh come on, you two," Mr. Gillespie said with a smile. "After all, we're among friends. You sound like you're explaining something to the PTA. Of course, I know your subjects are important. But really, would it make any difference if Barbara missed a few class sessions? It might be different with some other students, but this girl has a lot at stake. It could make the difference between whether or not she gets a scholarship. She simply doesn't have time to participate in other extracurricular activities. And the leadership experience in the band will be valuable in her future career. Do you mean to say that you would give Physical Education and Health priority over this type of experience for Barbara Martin?"

Gregory Coleman listened to the last remarks of the Guidance Director with increasing signs of irritation. "If I hear you right, you're saying that Health and Physical Education are really not important enough to matter. Would you make the same statements if Barbara had to skip Mathematics two or three times a week? After all, it meets every day, and she is an honor student, and she could do her assignments outside of class."

"Of course not," the Guidance Counselor replied, "but Math is a solid academic subject, and I don't see how you can compare either the content of the course or its importance to her future. She can't get into college at all without Math. But whether or not she has Health and Physical Education doesn't really make any difference. Personally, I don't see how you can draw an analogy between Math and P. E."

Mrs. Dailey asked, "Doesn't this student have a study hall or some other elective that would give her some leeway in working out her schedule so that she can complete her Health and Physical Education requirement?"

"That's just the problem," explained Mr. Gillespie. "Her four solid subjects are honors sections, and they cannot be changed. She doesn't have a study period because Barbara's parents want her to take Driver education and Typing for College Bound Students. These courses are only offered during the fall term for academic students. There really is no way we can shift things."

"Well, in that case, I would say that one of those electives will have to go," Mr. Coleman stated. "I certainly don't intend to sit by idly and have Physical Education and Health treated like some orphan in the curriculum. Why is it that when educators define the goals of education, they always list health as number one? But when they start working out the curriculum, they don't think it's important enough to consider it as a requirement! Well, I've seen enough of this around here in the past. And now I'm in a position to rectify the situation, and I intend to start right now, with no exceptions from the very beginning. A requirement is a requirement! So far as I am concerned I am not permitting Mrs. Dailey to excuse Barbara from her requirement in Physical Education and Health. You'll just have to work out some other plan with the girl"

"O.K., Don," the Guidance Counselor answered. "Barbara cannot be excused without your permission. I can't say that I agree with you in this instance, but you're the boss. I'll call Barbara in and see what we can work out."

As Mr. Coleman rose to leave, Mrs. Dailey said, "My goodness, I didn't mean to stir up such a hornet's nest during the first week of a new job. I hope the next time we talk, it will be under more pleasant conditions."

The next morning, Mr. Coleman and Mrs. Dailey were asked to report to the Principal's office immediately after school dismissal. When they entered his office the Principal said, "I have a letter here that was brought in by Barbara Martin. I think you will be interested in its contents." He handed the letter over to Mr. Coleman and Mrs. Dailey who read the following:

Dear Dr. Enders:
Barbara has told us of the difficulties she is having in scheduling her fall courses so that she can participate in the marching band. According to what she has told us, everything hinges upon an adjustment that could be made in Physical Education and Health. As we understand it, however, neither the Physical Education Department Chairman nor her teacher is willing to excuse Barbara for the short period of time that she must be present at the band practices.
Mr. Gillespie has suggested that she drop either Typing or Driver Education, since these are electives. We would

like to point out that this is Barbara's last opportunity to take these courses, both of which we believe are of great importance to her. We want her to have them.

Although we understand the viewpoint of the Physical Education Department, we feel that Barbara's case is worthy of consideration. There has been precedent for excusing students from Physical Education and Health in the past. One of our neighbor's boys didn't have to fulfill this requirement for graduation. Please understand that we are not asking that Barbara be excused from the requirement, but merely that she be allowed to miss classes for the short time that the band is practicing during the football season and prior to the statewide competition. We feel that she will surely be getting plenty of exercise during those practices. And as far as Health is concerned, she will be in class once a week, and we guarantee she will keep up with the work assigned on the other two days when she misses class. On Dec. 1st she will be able to resume her normal schedule.

We would very much appreciate your giving our request serious consideration. We would like to discuss this with you further, if it becomes necessary.

Sincerely,

JOHN MARTIN

After reading the letter Mr. Coleman and Mrs. Dailey looked up at the Principal who said to them, "I wonder if there is anything we can do to help Barbara?"

DISCUSSION QUESTIONS

1. How do you account for the Guidance Counselor's attitude toward Health Education and Physical Education? How prevalent do you think this attitude is today?

2. Comment on Coach Leo's attitude toward Health Education and Physical Education.

3. Do you think the practice of scheduling Health and Physical Education as a unit is desirable?

4. Discuss the connotations of the following terms relating to high school courses: Hygiene; Health Education; Gym; Physical Education.

5. What do you think of the grading practices for Health and Physical Education in this case? Are there other subjects in the curriculum which have similar grading practices?

6. Do you think Health Education should be required of all high school students?

7. Discuss the relative values of Typing, Driver Education, Physical Education and Hygiene for Barbara Martin both now and in the future.

8. Should honor students have special privileges in the scheduling of their classes and attendance?

9. What do you think of Mrs. Dailey's philosophy of teaching Health Education?

10. Comment on the relationships between the Chairmen of the Guidance Department, the Health and Physical Education Department and the Principal in this case. How does the request from Barbara Martin's parents affect these relationships?

11. Do you think the Martins' request is reasonable?

12. If you were Mr. Coleman, how would you respond to the Principal's question?

Selected References

The School Health Issue: Health Education as a Requirement.

American Association for Health, Physical Education and Recreation. *School Health Practices in the United States*, Washington, D.C., The Association. 1961.

Anderson, C.L.: *School Health Practice*. 3rd Ed., St. Louis, The C.V. Mosby Co., 1964. (Chapters 11 and 14).

Byrd, Oliver: *School Health Administration*, Philadelphia, W. B. Saunders Co., 1964. (Chapter 7, The Health Curriculum; Chapter 22, Health and Physical Education).

Bucher, Charles A.: *Administration of School Health and Physical Education Programs*, 3rd Ed., St. Louis, The C.V. Mosby Co., 1963.

Grout, Ruth: *Health Teaching in Schools*, 4th Ed., Philadelphia, W.B. Saunders Co., 1963.

Herman, W.W.: Required Health and Family Life Education in Schools. J.A.M.A. *198*: 749–752, 1966.

Irwin, L.W. and Mayshark, C.: *Health in Secondary Schools*, St. Louis, The C.V. Mosby Co., 1964.

Joint Committee on Health Problems in Education of the National Education Association and the American Medical Association: Washington, D.C and Chicago, *Suggested School Health Policies*, 4th Ed., 1966. (Chapter II, School Health Education; Chapter IV, Health Aspects of Physical Education).

Joint Committee on Health Problems in Education of the National Education Association and the American Medical Association: Washington D.C. and Chicago, *Why Health Education?* 1965.

Kilander, H.F.: Health Education as College Entrance Unit., J. School Health, *27*:149, 1951.

Kilander, H.F.: *School Health Education*, New York, The Macmillan Co., 1962.

Mayshark, Cyrus and Shaw, Donald D.: *Administration of School Health Programs*, St. Louis, The C.V. Mosby Co., 1967. (Chapter 6, Instructional Component).

Moss, Bernice: Can Health Education Command Academic Respect? J. School Health. *28*: 26 and 58, 1957.

Nemir, Alma: *The School Health Program*, Philadelphia, W.B. Saunders Co., 1959. (Chapter 20. School Health Education).

Oberteuffer, Delbert and Beyrer, Mary K.: *School Health Education.* 4th Ed., New York, Harper & Row, 1965.

Report of the Seventh National Conference on Physicians and Schools. American Medical Association, Chicago, 1959. (pp. 18-30. Time for Teaching Health and Physical Education. pp. 66-83. Standards of Study for Health Education.)

Sliepcevich, E.M.: Responsibility of the Physical Educator for Health Instruction. JOHPER *32*: 32-33, 1961.

The School Health Education Study: A Summary Report, Washington, D.C., The School Health Education Study, 1964.

Smolensky, Jack and Bonvechio, L. Richard: *Principles of School Health*. Boston, D.C. Heath and Co., 1966. (Chapter 2. Basic Issues and Problems in School Health. Chapter 7. Health Instruction).

The Commission on Philosophy for School Health Education, A Point of View for School Health Education. JOHPER, *35*: 26, 1962.

The School Health Education Study, *Health Education: A Conceptual Approach to Curriculum Design*, St. Paul, Minnesota Mining and Manufacturing Co., 1967. 141 pp.

Thompson, John C.: Room for Health Education. JOHPER *26*:45, 1955.

Reporting Practices

Bollenbacher, Joan: *Student Records and Reports — Elementary and Secondary*, *Encyclopedia of Educational Research*, (ed.) Chester W. Harris. 3rd Ed., New York, The Macmillan Co., 1960. pp. 1437-1442.

Elsbree, Willard S., McNally, Harold J. and Wynn, Richard: *Elementary School Administration and Supervision*. 3rd Ed., New York, American Book Co., 1967. Chapter 17. School Records).

French, Will, Hull. J. Dan and Dodds, B.L.: *American High School Administration*. New York, Rinehart & Co., 1957. (pp. 355-365. School Marks and Promotional Practices).

Organizational References

American Association for Health, Physical Education and Recreation, 1201 Sixteenth St., N.W. Washington, D.C. 20006

American Medical Association, 533 North Dearborn Street, Chicago, Illinois 60610

National Council on Alcoholism, 2 East 103rd Street, New York, New York

U.S. Department of Health, Education and Welfare, Washington, D.C. 20025 (Children's Bureau, Office of Education, Public Health Service)

2

One For
The Road

WHO'S WHO

JOHN POWERS   *Superintendent of Schools, Dexter*

DR. BRUCE EVANS
MRS. MARY FORESTER
KENNETH DALTON   *Members of the Board of Education,*
ROBERT EGAN   *Dexter*
MELVIN MEYER

17

Following a tragic automobile accident, a suburban school district re-examines the issue of what to do about alcohol education.

"THANK you very much for that fine introduction, Professor Heller. I find it hard to recognize myself through all those flattering remarks. At any rate, I want you to know what a pleasure it is for a school superintendent to try to project some of the reality of what many of you may be experiencing before long.

"When he called me about a month ago, Professor Heller suggested that I highlight the relationships between the school board, the school administration and the community. Well, I began to think about what might be the best way to do this in a one-night stand. It occurred to me that a description of what took place in a community not too far from here several years ago might just fill the bill and give us all a chance to consider some solutions to practical problems of administration.

"This incident was related to me by the Superintendent of Schools. Let's call him John Powers, and we'll call the community Dexter. I'll tell you the story as I remember him telling it to me. When the incident happened, Powers had been in Dexter about twelve years — long enough to see lots of changes, some good, some bad — but mostly the kinds of changes that have been occurring in other towns and cities that have become bedroom communities for cities like Metropolis. Being over 35 miles away from the city, Dexter people used to think theirs was a town with a difference — the difference being a bit of that home town feeling you get when most of the people work in the same place where they live. Oh, Dexter always had some commuters, but when Powers first arrived there, commuters comprised only about a fourth of all the employed people, mostly those living in the new development in the north end of town.

"At the time of the incident I'm going to relate, new people, largely from the city, had been moving into Dexter over a period of ten years. When they came to register their children in school, Dr. Powers told me that they almost invariably mentioned as their major reason for moving so far away from the city 'to get better education for their kids'. Dexter did have a reputation for having fine schools, and Powers surmised that some of the folks thought they would get away from the complicated problems of the city schools. Most of these new Dexter residents seemed to be comfortably fixed. They could afford to buy or build new houses. And they seemed to feel good about doing something that they thought would be good for their kids. Powers estimated that well over half of the employed people — men, and women, too — took the train to-and-from the city every day.

"There had been some resentment between the oldtimers and the newcomers in Dexter. Powers said that he did not consider this unusual, but it did create some tensions. The city people who had moved out there to what they liked to call the 'country' had some rather sophisticated ways. They were accustomed to a way of life that placed high value on social activity — not only for the adults, but also for the young people. It was apparent that the kids were encouraged by these parents to date at an early age and to participate in other activities that had not been permitted to children.

of the old guard of Dexter who had a different tradition in bringing up their youngsters. The drinking that was known to be practiced by some teen-agers, the reputed sexual promiscuity, and the constant drive to do more things that used to be reserved for adulthood had been slowly increasing among the new, and even some of the old. As a school administrator, Powers worried a bit about these kids and their behavior and thought of the inconsistency between the values the school tried to put across and the ones that some parents were supporting. But he realized that when parents gave their approval — or at least, didn't give their disapproval — the school was in a difficult position to try to effect changes.

"Sooner or later something was bound to happen that would 'blow the lid' off the powder keg, and something did. There was a party for a group of seniors at one of the new big homes. It was an elaborate affair, and started out with cocktails served by a professional bartender whom the parents had hired for the occasion. The drinking went on for a couple of hours before an elegant dinner was finally served to the young people. It was reported later that a number of the young guests got 'high' from consuming more alcohol than they could handle, and some went to sleep right there and never got home that night. But the tragedy of the party and the evening was that a couple left the party, raced down the highway in a fast sports car, ran off the road, hit a tree, demolished the car and badly injured both of them. It was a sobering experience for the whole community. The two students were reported to have consumed quite a few cocktails at the party and to have been quite unsteady as they left the house. Powers guessed he'd never know all the facts, because some parents, and students, too, tried to cover up when they realized the awful implications.

"It was not only a matter of a horrible incident, but there were also legal considerations. The parents of the boy at the house where the party was held were at home at the time, and with full knowledge of the ages of these young people, were serving them cocktails, a violation of the law prohibiting the serving of liquor to minors. Powers suspected at the time that there would eventually be a court trial.

"The whole community was shocked — and many were ashamed. They had a lot of publicity. The news was carried in the papers of Metropolis as well as in Dexter's own Daily Banner.

"It was a funny thing, though. People who never cared anything about the curriculum before — and especially the health curriculum — were suddenly rising up and publicly pointing the finger at the schools saying, 'What are our children being taught about alcohol? If the schools did more about teaching health, this tragic thing might never have happened.' The high school PTA, a mere handful of dedicated parents, asked for information about this. And Powers had calls from several of the community religious leaders urging that the schools 'do something that might change the teen-agers' social behavior'.

"The School Board members had about as many calls as Powers did. They felt that they were on the spot and had better discuss the situation and perhaps come up with a plan.

"While it wasn't part of the agenda for the next Board meeting, Powers heard through the grapevine that there would be a lot of town people attending to bring up the subject during the open part of the meeting. There was supposed to be a delegation from the Women's Club with a petition to demand that the schools do more teaching about the effects of alcohol. People were really stirred up.

"This awful incident had brought some other matters to the fore too. Powers didn't know how much was fact and how much fiction, but there was talk about marijuana users in Dexter — some of them school children. Powers asked his guidance director and the school physician about this, and they agreed that there was a possibility that a small group of students were smoking 'pot', but there was no real evidence. People seemed to be gripped with a fear that their children might succumb to using some of these things. And Powers, too, had real feelings of guilt for doing so little about it in the schools. He wasn't surprised that some parents should blame the schools for their inadequacies — that was easier than admitting one's own failures as parents. Powers told me he had a bit of anxiety about the next Board meeting which was slated to be held in two weeks. He wondered what major issues would be brought up and what demands would be made by those attending.

"As a rule, the Board had not spent much time on curriculum. It had more pressing problems of constructing enough schools to house the growing population. And the Board also gave a lot of attention to the Teacher's Association demands for improved salaries. By and large, the Board felt that the curriculum could best be determined by the educators, though now and then the members prodded Powers to upgrade the offerings in foreign languages, mathematics and science. Almost all of the Board members were keenly aware of the competition to get into college and they wanted Dexter kids to be well prepared so they would be accepted by the colleges they wanted. Some of the teachers thought the administration was going a little overboard on this at the expense of the boys and girls who were not college bound, and Dexter had its share of those. Nevertheless, the schools were experimenting with French for all children starting at the fourth grade. They were utilizing educational television for this since the District didn't have enough fourth grade teachers who were qualified to teach the language.

"The schools were also trying out team teaching,

and they had a new language laboratory in the high school. Articles about many aspects of the Dexter educational program had been published in educational journals and Powers was rather proud of the school System's progress. But he realized he still had plenty of problems. He suspected that the next Board meeting might bring some of these to light.

"If Powers knew exactly what issues would be raised, he might have been better prepared to guide the Board. As far as he could see, the only issue was whether or not the school was fulfilling its responsibilities in teaching about alcohol, tobacco, drugs and other aspects of health. If so, was the teaching effective?

"Fortunately, the school system had been part of a national study on health instruction a few years previously when a complete survey of the situation was made. I have a summary of those findings here and I'd like to read them to you.

Information About the Dexter Health Education Curriculum

Health has always been considered to be an important educational objective. The curriculum has been developed to provide basic information about health and to encourage young people to make wise decisions about health matters, in this way contributing to the achievement of their own life goals.

The Dexter elementary schools include kindergarten through the sixth grade. Health instruction is a part of the curriculum at every grade level. It is correlated and integrated with other subjects, largely with reading and with physical education. Emphasis is on developing personal habits of health and safety and teachers take every opportunity to utilize those "teachable moments" that occur during the day. Readers have some health content and these are supplemented by library books and by supplementary materials occasionally provided by health agencies.

In the secondary school, Dexter requires that all high school sophomores take Health Education for a full year's period. It is offered two or three days a week (50-minute periods), alternating with Physical Education. Girls and boys are separated and the class is taught by the physical education teachers. One credit is given for the required sophomore Health Education course. Some health content is also included in Home Economics and Biology, and, on occasion, in Social Studies when there is some focus on community health.

The Physical Education teachers who handle the health course have state certification in Health and Physical Education, which means that they have had at least six credit hours of college preparation in health education in addition to background courses such as anatomy and physiology. In addition to their teaching assignments in the two subjects (Health and Physical Education) these faculty members are also resoponsible for coaching and supervision of intramural athletics. Health is taught in a regular classroom.

Health content can be described as follows:

GRADES 1 — 3   Accident Prevention
                Cleanliness and Grooming
                Dental Health
                Food
                Exercise and Relaxation
GRADES 4 — 5   Posture and Body Mechanics
                Rest and Sleep
                Vision and Hearing
                Communicable Diseases
                (Also some review of units included
                previously.)
GRADE 6   Family Life
                Personality Development
                Alcohol
                Smoking
HIGH SCHOOL   Structure and Function of Body
   (*Required* Boy — Girl Relationships
   courses)   Smoking
                Alcohol
                Drugs and Narcotics
                Mental Health and Personal Adjustment

This survey had resulted in a few recommendations and even a few changes, but there were still plenty of problems in the area of health. Few people wanted to teach it. Some of those who were teaching health there were not fully qualified — they were primarily physical educators with only minimum preparation in hygiene. But the only practical approach to scheduling required tying Health and Physical Education together. Dexter schools were like a lot of others in this respect. They had Health Education as a required subject for high school sophomores who took it alternately with Physical Education meeting two or three days a week for a full year. Instruction about alcohol was mandated by the State Education Department, so Powers felt certain that it was included in the course.

"The elementary curriculum supervisor emphasized the idea that every teacher must teach health. These classroom teachers relied mainly on a series of recently published health texts that were adopted as a result of the health instruction survey. A curriculum innovation inspired by the same survey was the additition of two elective health courses at the high school level: one in Safety and First Aid, and the other in Home Nursing. Many of the youngsters who elected these were from the non-college bound group; the others just didn't have time in their schedules for them.

"Powers could remember some of the comments of the Board members when these courses were added. There was Melvin Meyer, sales manager for a large company that handles office machines. A real hustler. Then there was Robert Egan, a local self-made grocer, and economy minded. Both were adamant about keeping 'frills' out of the system. Egan had told Powers, 'If kids want to learn this stuff, they can take it at the Red Cross. Why should we have to stand the added expense at a time when the tax rate is going up?'

"We finally convinced them that it wouldn't add to the school costs. One of the nurses was qualified to teach the classes and had the time to do it. She got a lot of help from the Red Cross and the schools had enough students taking the courses to keep them going.

"Ken Dalton was the only other Board member at

the time of the incident who was also serving when they instituted the new courses. He managed a life insurance company in Metropolis, but had lived in Dexter all his life. He seemed to resent some of the new people who had been moving in, and kept saying, 'These nouveau riche and their big ideas about college. We ought to be looking out for the kids who aren't going to college — offer them something practical that they can use.' He had solidly supported the new health courses and helped influence the others to approve the plan. That wasn't too hard since no budget increases were involved.

"The most recent additions to the Board, Mary Forester, a community-minded housewife, and Dr. Bruce Evans, a local dermatologist, had been generally supportive of the schools and had fought off numerous attempts by a community group to save money by increasing class size. Mrs. Forester and Dr. Evans had been serving on the Board for only three months, but even in that short time had been suggesting and supporting the idea of a stronger academic program in mathematics and the languages. Mrs. Forester was 100% behind the elementary school French program and wanted to broaden the range of languages offered in the Dexter High School. She claimed that there were enough interested students to organize a four-year sequence in Latin. She'd had quite a bit of it at Vassar herself, and would have liked for her children to have the opportunity to take it.

"As Powers thought about his five Board members, he wondered what their response might be to community pressure for improving the health curriculum. Of course, he couldn't be sure, but he didn't think Mrs. Forester would be too receptive to any such ideas that might be forthcoming. He'd heard Mary Forester say, in front of her high school daughter, that 'this health class is just a waste of time. Carol knows all she needs to know about cleanliness and diet and those things, and she didn't learn it at school. I think parents have the responsibility for certain aspects of their children's education, and I don't think the school should hold these health classes even though some parents may be delinquent about their own responsibility'. Dr. Evans, since he was in the health field himself, might react differently. Powers just didn't know.

"Well, that's the gist of an incident that put Dexter on the map in a most unfavorable way and forced its Board of Education, the administration and the community to give some serious consideration to the health curriculum there. You are well aware of the issue of what is the home's responsibility and what is the school's responsibility in the area of health. This has plagued educators for a long time. It doesn't seem to be a clear-cut case. And the fact that there is so little health teaching, much of it poorly done by unqualified teachers, is evidence that the general public as a rule, does not really support it. They didn't in Dexter. But you know, if you tried to move Science out of the curriculum, or if you offered it on a one day a week basis, you'd have the whole town on your neck! But not so with Health.

"Now, the usual rationale for including health in the curriculum is that it is an important part of education, contributes to one's ability to learn, and will help anyone achieve his goals — whatever they may be. If we include health teaching in schools, we must be convinced that the school is the best place to provide this education. I could tell you what happened in Dexter with respect to the health curriculum and what steps Powers took. But I think that it would be more interesting and hopefully, more educational, if I posed a number of questions to you to help get some answers to the can of worms opened by an "extra one for the road":

DISCUSSION QUESTIONS

1. Can teaching about alcohol be effective when it is in conflict with what is socially acceptable by a large segment of the community?

2. What do you think should be the objectives of alcohol education in schools? In the home?

3. Can these objectives be applied to other aspects of health education such as sex education, smoking and use of narcotics and other drugs?

4. Comment on the qualifications of the health education teachers.

5. Should Health be a required subject? If so, at what grade level(s)?

6. If you were John Powers, what would you do in preparation for the Board meeting scheduled two weeks hence:
   a. with the community?
   b. with the school Board members?
   c. with the administration and teaching staff?

Selected References

The School Health Issue: The Adequacy of Health Instruction.

American Association for Health, Physical Education and Recreation, Commission on Philosophy for School Health Education: A Point of View on School Health Education, JOHPER, *33*:24-26, 1962.

American Assciation for Health, Physical Education and Recreation, Professional Preparation in Health Education, Physical Education and Recreation, Recommendations of a National Conference. 1962. 176 pp.

Anderson, C.L.: *School Health Practice*, 3rd Ed., St. Louis, The C.V. Mosby Co., 1964. (Chapters 11, 12, 13, 14, 15. Health Instruction).

Block, Marvin A.: Teen-Age Drinking: Whose Responsibility? Today's Health, *39*: 21, 1961.

Byrd, Oliver E.: *School Health Administration*, Philadelphia, W.B. Saunders Co., 1964. (Chapter 12 — The School Health Educator; Chapter 7 — The Health Curriculum; Chapter 5 — School Health Law).

Curriculum Commission, Health Education Division, *Health Concepts: Guides for Health Instruction*, Washington, D.C., American Association for Health, Physical Education and Recreation, 1967. 52 pp.

Freeman, H.E. and Scott, J.F.: A Critical Review of Alcohol Education for Adolescents, Community Mental Health, 2: 222-230, 1966.

Haag, Jessie Helen: *School Health Program*, New York, Henry Holt and Company, 1958. (Part 7 — Health Instruction. Chapter 30 — State Laws Influencing the School Health Program).

Joint Committee on Health Problems in Education of the National Education Association and the American Medical Association, *Health Education*, Washington, D.C., the National Education Association, 1961

Kilander, H.F.: *School Health Education: A Study of Content, Methods and Materials*. New York, The Macmillan Co., 1962. 500 pp.

McCarthy, Raymond G. (Ed.): *Alcohol Education for Classroom and Community*, New York, McGraw-Hill Book Co., 1964. 323 pp.

Mayshark, Cyrus and Shaw, Donald: *Administration of School Health Programs*, St. Louis, The C.V. Mosby Co., 1967. (Chapter 6. Instructional Component.)

National Committee on School Health Policies, *Suggested School Health Policies*, Washington, D.C., National Education Association and Chicago, American Medical Association, 1967. (Chapter I. School Health Education.)

Report of the Seventh National Conference on Physicians and Schools. American Medical Association, Bureau of Health Education, Chicago, Ill., 1959. (Time for Teaching Health and Physical Education, pp. 18-37; Standards of Study for Health Education, pp. 66-83)

School Health Education Study: *Health Education: A Conceptual Approach to Curriculum Design*, St. Paul, Minnesota Mining and Manufacturing Co., 1967. 141 pp.

Sliepcevich, E.M.: *School Health Education Study: a Summary Report*, Washington, D.C., School Health Education Study, 1964.

Smolensky, Jack and Bonvechio, L. Richard: *Principles of School Health*, Boston, D.C. Heath Co., 1966. (Chapters 6 and 7 — Health Curriculum Development and Instruction; p. 292, The Law and the Curriculum).

Teamwork in School Health, Washington, D.C., American Assocation for Health, Physical Education and Recreation, 1962.

Todd, Frances: *Teaching About Alcohol*, New York, McGraw-Hill Book Co., 1965, 240 pp.

School-Community Relations

Carter, Richard F., Suttoff, John Newell, Dwight H., Savard, William G. and Trusty, Francis M.: *Communications and Their Schools,* School of Education, Stanford University, Stanford, California, 1960.

Elsbree, Willard S., McNally, Harold J. and Wynn, Richard: *Elementary School Administration and Supervision.* 3rd Ed., New York, American Book Co., 1967. (Objectives of School-Community Relations, pp. 341-371.)

Finn, James D.: The Good Guys and the Bad Guys, Phi Delta Kappan, *40*: 2-5, 29-32, 1959.

Grieder, Calvin, Pierce, Ruman M., and Rosenstengel, William E.: *Public School Administration,* New York, The Ronald Press Co. (Participation of the Community in Educational Affairs, pp. 609-620.)

Hamburg, Marian V.: Working with Community Agencies on School Health Programs, J. School Health, *36*: 487-492, 1966.

Hand, Harold C.: *Principles of Public Secondary Education,* New York, Harcourt, Brace, 1958. (Maintaining Good School-Community Relations, pp. 114-139.)

Kindred, Leslie W.: *School Public Relations,* Englewood Cliffs, N.J., Prentice-Hall, 1957. (Chapters 1, 2, 5.)

Knezevich, Stephen J.: *Administration of Public Education,* New York, Harper and Row, 1962. (Chapter 16.)

Willower, Donald J.: *Lay and Professional Decisions in Education,* Peabody J. Education, *41*: 226-228, 1964.

Wilson, Robert E.: *Eductional Administration,* Columbus, Ohio, Charles E. Merrill, 1966. (pp. 386-402. The Nature and Importance of Communication.)

Related Background Reading

Adler, Irving: *What We Want of Our Schools,* New York, John Day Co. Inc. (Chapter VI. Moral Values and Juvenile Delinquency).

Bronfenbrenner, Urie: The Split-Level American Family, Saturday Review, October 7, 1967. pp. 60-66.

Bruner, Jerome S.: *The Process of Education,* New York, Vintage Books, 1960.

Cain, Arthur H.: *Young People and Drinking,* New York, The John Day Co., 1963.

Coleman, James S.: *The Adolescent Society,* New York, The Free Press of Glencoe (Macmillan), 1961.

Downey, Lawerence W.: *The Secondary Phase of Education*, New York, Blaisdell Publishing Co., (Ginn & Co.) 1965. (The Informal Group and Sub-Cultural Group. pp. 137-141.)

French, Will, Hull, J. Dan, and Dodds, B.L.: *American High School Administration — Policy and the Practice*, New York, Rinehart & Co., (The School Studies the Community and Its Youth. pp. 531-557)

Friedenberg, Edgar Z.: *Coming of Age in America*, New York, Random House, 1965.

Good, H.G.: A History of American Education, New York, The Macmillan Co., 1962. (High School Inquiries. pp. 546-549.)

Musgrove, F.: *Youth and the Social Order*, Bloomington, Indiana, The University of Indiana Press, 1965.

Nordstrom, Carl, Friedenberg, Edgar Z. and Gold, Hilary A.: *Society's Children: A Study of Resentement in the Secondary School*, New York, Random House, 1967.

Reiss, Albert J., Jr. (Ed.): *Schools in a Changing Society*, New York, The Free Press of Glencoe (The Macmillan Co.), 1965. (Chapter 4. The Youth Culture, The School System and the Socialization Community.)

Watenberg, William W. (Ed.): Social Deviancy Among Youth. Chicago, National Society for the Study of Education, 65th Yearbook, Part 1, 1966.

Wellington, C. Burleigh and Wellington, Jean: *Teaching for Critical Thinking*, New York, McGraw-Hill Book Co., 1960. (Chapter 3. Adolescents and Adolescence.)

Organizational References

American Association for Health, Physical Education and Recreation, 1201 Sixteenth St., N.W., Washington, D.C. 20006.

National Council on Alcoholism, 2 East 103rd Street, New York, New York.

U.S. Department of Health, Education and Welfare, Washington, D.C., 20025 (Children's Bureau, Office of Education, Public Health Service).

3

It's Only Natural

33

*The health education curriculum becomes
the target of a community group which
challenges the validity of its contents.*

IT'S hard to say whether the students or the teachers
of North Bend enjoy the annual Teachers Institute most.
For the students it is a welcome October holiday from
school. For the teachers it is a day off, not a holiday,
but a chance to participate in professional meetings on
a variety of educational topics. North Bend prides itself
on its schools and its reputation for leadership in new
educational approaches. The Institute usually provides
a showcase for the new projects and experimental
approaches being tried out in the system. Teachers
often remarked about the difficulty of deciding which
program to attend.

With the appointment of a new superintendent four
years ago, North Bend's fame for educational trail-blaz-
ing had begun to extend outside of its region and had
attracted the interest of some national education groups
as well. The system had been selected, for instance, as
the site for two national pilot projects: one, a study of
low-achievers, which had just been started; and the other,
a try-out of an experimental curriculum in health education. This curriculum study, underway for two full years,
was one of the features of the current Teachers Institute.
The plan for the session included a demonstration by
two of the sixth grade teachers who had been involved,
both of whom were extremely enthusiastic about the
program's emphasis on the development of critical

thinking about current health issues of importance to children. As Edith Mitchell, the Health Coordinator for the District, had often explained, "There's no preaching in this approach — there isn't even any lecturing. The teachers and the kids determine the problems to be studied and then they plan how to go about finding the information they need. But after that, it is up to the kids to find the answers for themselves — not from some dry, possibly outdated, texts and encyclopedias, but from all kinds of sources, especially from knowledgeable people. It's amazing how interested kids become when this approach is used, and how convinced they become about current health issues when they dig up their own information and learn how to evaluate it."

Although only one school in the North Bend District was involved in the experimental curriculum, all the teachers in the system had heard about it, since it was not the kind of program that was quietly conducted within classroom walls or even contained in a single building. Participating students had made their presences known as they fanned out into the community investigating a variety of health problems. It was no great surprise to Edith Mitchell, then, to notice that the Little Theatre, where the health education session was scheduled, began to fill up early. As she stood at the outer door, greeting her colleagues, she had a feeling of pride as she thought to herself, "I would never have believed that some of these teachers would come to a health meeting. I know some of them think the subject is useless and a waste of time."

She felt confident that the presentation would go well, because it had been carefully planned. In addition to a brief description of the experimental curriculum, there was to be a panel of experts who would provide the content background for the teachers' demonstration of methodology that would follow. She could hear Mary Hall and Jeanette Starr, the two sixth-grade teachers involved, talking together as they were setting up the materials to be exhibited as part of their demonstration. They were excited by the opportunity to describe their work, and this had been heightened by a visit to one of them the day previously by a reporter from a local paper. "It was after school and the children had all left," Jeanette Starr had told Miss Mitchell over the phone the night before. "I was getting some materials ready for our presentation when this woman came in — I'm not sure what paper she is with — but she wanted some information about our experimental curriculum in health, and particularly about the food buying session to be discussed at the Institute program. She seemed very interested and stayed quite a long time. I showed her the materials we had been using and described how the kids had gone into various stores to check prices, quality and quantity of certain foods. I told her that the kids had learned a lot about getting the most value for their money and had their eyes opened about overcharging and misrepresentation of products, misleading advertising, et cetera. I also told her I thought that they know now how hard it is to be intelligent consumers. I'm sure they have a new appreciation of what their parents go through in buying for the family. I gave her some samples of the new materials on quackery from the A.M.A. — we had some extras and she was so interested in them. I'm sure we'll get a good write-up. I can hardly wait to see it."

"You certainly managed to get community involvement, Jeanette," Edith Mitchell had said to her. "No one can say our curriculum is not based on reality!"

And now it was almost time for the Institute program to begin. The last few people were entering the Little Theatre.

"You don't mind if I tape this session, do you?" queried one of them.

Edith Mitchell, recognizing a high school teacher of

whose name she was uncertain, smiled and answered, "Of course not. As a matter of fact, it's a good idea — one I should have thought of myself. Maybe I'll be wanting to borrow that tape from you. You're Miss Gibbons, aren't you?"

"Yes, I'm Jean Gibbons — High School English," she replied as she continued to move into the Theatre with the others.

A few minutes after the scheduled 10 A.M. starting time Miss Mitchell greeted the assembled group. "I'm so glad to see so many of you here today. We have tough competition, I know, with some of the fascinating topics being presented in other sessions. After our program is over, we hope you'll be as enthusiastic about our experimental health curriculum as we are. Let me start by giving you some background.

"What you are going to hear and see is in two parts. First, we have a panel of experts who will discuss 'Nutrition Facts for the Intelligent Consumer.' They will present some of the same content that our 6th grade youngsters have been studying. For the past month and a half these children have been concerned with just one problem: how to make decisions about foods and other health products that are purchased. Of course, this requires learning how to judge a value. As we all know, a bargain is not always a saving of money. So, they investigated for themselves, comparing different products to see how they measured up to the criteria they had developed from references and resources set out by various scientific groups and authoritative personnel. We hope the end result is a group of knowledgeable youngsters who know how to select foods that they buy — now and throughout life.

"Our new approach depends upon student learning activities. It is really problem solving related to health problems of concern to youngsters. I don't want to steal their stuff, but after the panel is finished, you will hear

from Mary Hall and Jeanette Starr. As two of the
teachers involved in this try-out, they spent part of one
summer in a workshop preparing for this new approach
before we instituted it a little more than a year ago.
I know they have interesting stories about their experiences with the curriculum.

"Now I would like to present our panel. Each
member will describe the role of his organization in
protecting the consumer and also discuss current problems in this area, including their suggestions about
educating children. All of us who are involved in this
experimental curriculum are indebted to these four
panelists who have been our major resources in this
study of how to spend food dollars wisely. I am happy
to welcome Dr. Bernard Warner from the North Bend
Medical Society; and next to him, Mr. Leonard Worth
from the F.D.A. office here — that's the Food and Drug
Administration; Miss Martha Noble, the Director of
Nutrition from our State Health Department, and Mrs.
Frank McCoy of the Better Business Bureau. Their comments will serve as a basis, then, for the demonstration
that will follow when Miss Mary Hall and Miss Jeanette
Starr tell you about their experiences in dealing with
this unit. They have some slides and other audio-visuals
to illustrate their presentation. And finally, we will
welcome questions, comments and discussion from all
of you."

For about 30 minutes the panelists discussed the
current problems in consumer protection and explained
the role of their organizations. They had each helped
in some way with the unit, either in planning, speaking
to a class, being interviewed by a student committee or
providing materials. Each panelist expressed amazement
at the amount of understanding and appreciation sixth
graders seemed to have gained from the learning experiences. "I never would have believed that kids would
get such insights into how to judge foods by comparing

labels so carefully," Miss Noble said. "I really believe the next generation of parents will be much better food shoppers, if this is any sample of what they are learning and I'm including future fathers. I didn't learn these things until college, and only because I was a Home Economics major."

Dr. Warner too, had praised the program. "You know, I really think we can lick some of the quackery that goes on if we can get more people to understand the things these kids do after the kinds of experiences they have had. These sixth graders won't be so prone to believe the claims of food faddists and unethical health practitioners that prey on their emotions — to get their dollars. This is the very kind of program that the Medical Society would like to see in every school. Their parents could use it too, I might add."

Then the two teachers took over. "We began on the first day," Miss Starr said, "with the question of 'Why do the hamburgers at Joe's cost less than the ones at the City Cafe?' Those are prices that my youngsters know about because they are certainly hamburger consumers. That one question led us into a discussion of possible reasons for price differences. We decided that we would find out for ourselves if Joe's hamburgers are really bigger than the Cafe's. And that meant setting up some standards for comparing the two, and then going out to find some of the answers.

"Some of my pupils actually interviewed Joe and also the manager of the City Cafe, using questions we developed in class concerning the meat, the buns, the pickles, the cost of labor, overhead, and all kinds of things. When they reported their findings, we were able to discuss some of the factors that influence the pricing of foods.

"They visited supermarkets, observed the different packages of ground meat and learned about the range of prices, and reasons for them. Also, they learned about government inspection of meat to make sure it is safe for human consumption. We didn't limit ourselves to meat — we compared other foods too: oleo and butter, for instance; all kinds of milk products; orange juice and synthetic orange drink. We learned about diet foods, and the various meanings of the word 'dietetic'. And we spent some time on foods that are labeled 'health foods'.

"The display you see over on the table is one that was developed by my class and represents their findings about health foods as compared with similar foods with no specific health claims. You can see some of the labels they collected and the advertising claims that went with the products. There is an interesting analysis of some ads they cut out of so-called 'health' magazines that they found on the newsstand. And when they wondered why these same products are not advertised in magazines that they have at home, we wrote letters to publishers and got statements of the criteria they use for accepting advertising. The whole thing was a revelation to all of us."

Mary Hall's story was similar to Jeanette Starr's and she displayed the same enthusiasm. "I never thought I would actually enjoy teaching health," she said, "but when you do it this way, it's really exciting. I was always a little afraid of the subject because there is so much I don't know, and health facts seem to change all the time. But we all learned together, and now we know where to go for reliable information about almost any phase of health, and that may be just as important as any of the facts.

"I don't want to take too much more time telling you about our unit, because you would probably rather ask questions, but I do want to let you hear, on tape, a dramatization that my group dreamed up. They were so impressed with the way some manufacturers, processors and dealers try to circumvent the laws by misrepresenting products, their value and their cost, that they decided to have a mock trial. And here's a part of it that I think you will enjoy."

She turned on the tape recorder and then came the strident voices of her sixth graders, one impersonating a judge; another, an accuser, a third, a defendant; and a string of witnesses in a trial of a health faddist for making false claims for his product: 'strength syrup'. There were laughs from the audience, and when it was over, a resounding applause. Then Miss Mitchell, smiling proudly, took charge and asked for questions or comments.

Almost immediately, Miss Gibbons, her face flushed, rose to her feet and said, "I am shocked by this whole presentation. In all of the remarks about foods no one pointed out what is happening to foods which are being grown in depleted soil. No one mentioned natural foods. You're not trying to educate; you're trying to control children's minds by controlling the information to which they have access. Where do you show them the great increase in chronic and degenerative diseases in our country — a situation that will worsen as long as we continue to poison ourselves with chemical fertilizers and synthetic foods. I'm not surprised that the A.M.A. is 100% behind this kind of teaching. Of course, they have a stake in it — it will hurt their business if people know the truth about natural foods and their healing and restorative properties. This whole demonstration reveals a monopolistic control of our children's minds. You present only one side of the question and apparently do it with full knowledge and intent. If you really weren't afraid of the truth, you would have one of the members of my organization on that panel today. But when we called the Superintendent's office last night to make the request, we got the brush off. 'It's too late to make changes; Dr. Herzog said. But, for your information, he did agree to meet with some of us next week, and believe me, this program will be challenged. Public schools can't be used to spread propaganda like this."

Miss Mitchell was stunned and her face showed it. She had time to regain her poise as Dr. Warner spoke up. "I don't know your name, young lady, but I assume you are a teacher. And since you mentioned the organization I represent, I would like to respond to you. I don't know what your group is, but I would suspect it promotes the so-called health foods. Your attack here today is similar to the emotional charges that others like you have been making on schools across the nation. Where is your evidence on whatever you're trying to push? What are your motives and why are you so enraged? If you have a proposal to make to the school about curriculum, there is an appropriate time, place and channel through which to do it. Why did you wait to come to this meeting to make vague charges? If you are a teacher in this system, it should not be news to you that this experimental program is being tried out — this is it's second year, and you must also be aware that it has the wholehearted support of a number of professional health organizations and other groups in the community who have been asked to participate. If you and your organization are so upset about it, why haven't you presented your convictions to the School authorities before so that they could be given consideration? You must know Miss Mitchell. Why didn't you talk with her? I'm sure she welcomes suggestions."

Miss Gibbons again rose to her feet and retorted angrily, "When they introduced this program, nothing was said about encouraging pupils to visit stores and make unreasonable demands upon the owners to defend their products and prices to kids whose minds had already been prejudiced. And that is exactly what has been happening in several food stores I know about. What kind of education do you call that?"

Miss Mitchell, who had regained her composure, said calmly, "Of course, we appreciate all points of view, Miss Gibbons, and I surely would like to talk with you further after the meeting. I wonder if there are others who wish to ask questions before we conclude?"

There were a few questions from other teachers concerning the time needed for the health education program and the amount of preparation required by the teachers. When these were answered, Miss Mitchell adjourned the meeting. She thanked the panelists and chatted with them briefly before they left. Then she took a minute to congratulate Mary Hall and Jeanette Starr for their presentations, but excused herself to find Miss Gibbons. There were groups of teachers still chatting in the hall, but Miss Gibbons was nowhere to be seen. A teacher standing nearby reported seeing Miss Gibbons leave the building.

As she stood there pondering what to do, Jeanette Starr, carrying exhibit materials to load into her car, stopped and said, "I'm really troubled by that high school teacher. I keep wondering what upset her so much. It's my class that has been digging into consumer aspects of food purchases, and they did visit the health food stores and did bring some interesting information. I didn't know that the owners of the stores were annoyed by the visits. If so, the youngsters didn't seem to realize it. But what I can't understand is why Miss Gibbons is so angry. With that chip on her shoulder, there's no telling what she might do."

"I must confess I'm a bit upset too," Miss Mitchell stated. "I'm going to call Dr. Herzog to see if he can tell us what it's all about — she mentioned a call to him. I'll keep you informed, but I'm sure there's nothing for you to worry about."

On the chance that the Assistant Superintendent in Charge of Curriculum might be in his office, Edith Mitchell drove to the administration building. She was pleased to find him pouring over a report as she looked in. He looked up, saw her in the doorway, and said, "Well, Edith, how did the big show go today?"

"I'm not sure, to tell the truth, and that's the very reason I'm here now." She proceeded to tell Dr. Herzog about Miss Gibbons and her tape recorder, and her angry charges at the end of the presentation. "She ended up by saying that a member of her organization, whatever it is, called you last night to try to get on the panel today. Is that so?"

Dr. Herzog responded. "Edith, I'm amazed at this. It is true that somone called — a man named White, I think, a member of a group, he said. I can't remember its exact name. As a matter of fact, I didn't think too much about it, or I would have called you. He wanted to get someone from his group on the panel because he said he had heard that the panel dealt nutrition and that it was very slanted. At the time, I couldn't imagine where he got his information. Anyway, I explained to him that I had no direct responsibility for the program, that it had been planned long in advance and that it was too late to make changes. I did tell him that I would be pleased to meet with him to discuss his complaint, which seemed to be that kids were coming into his store, reading labels and copying things down, asking lots of questions and buying nothing. And then, he said that something peculiar must be going on at school because a group of kids yelled 'quack quack' every time they pass his store. To tell the truth, I didn't take it very seriously, but maybe I should have. I didn't realize that Miss Gibbons was tied up with his outfit."

"I didn't know about it either, but come to think about it, I believe that Miss Gibbons' father used to operate a food store when he was alive."

"So that's the connection? Well, I really don't think there is anything we need to do right now. I set up a tentative date for a meeting with Mr. White, and I was planning to call you tomorrow to see whether it would be a convenient time for you to come. Let's see, we set it up for next Thursday at 3 o'clock. Could you be there?"

"Yes, that's all right with me."

"In view of this public explosion today, maybe we had better do a bit of planning. I have to call Mr. White anyway to confirm the date. Supposing I ask him if he is coming alone and what questions in particular he wants to discuss. I wonder if Miss Gibbons might be in on this too."

"I would suspect she is. I told her that I wanted to talk with her after the meeting, but she didn't wait. Do you think I should make it a point to go over to the High School to see her?"

"I don't think so. Since she didn't wait for you, she probably didn't want to talk with you — at least, not with you alone. Let me follow through with Mr. White and I'll let you know what I find out. In the meantime, it would be a good idea for you to talk with Miss Hall and Miss Starr to get as many details as possible about what has been going on inside and outside of their classrooms as a part of this study. We should have as much information as possible before the meeting."

Edith Mitchell left the building with a foreboding of trouble developing around a health curriculum that had excited her more than anything she had done in her 25 years in the education field. She thought about the tape recording, wondered why Miss Gibbons wanted it, and how she might use it.

The arrangements for the meeting were confirmed. Mr White and a colleague, Miss Jarvis, were expected. John Herzog had alerted Ethel Mitchell to the complaint that the schools are trying to "control children's minds," as Mr. White had put it, by controlling the materials the schools are using in the health education program. Dr. Herzog had also invited the Principal of the Allen School, where the curriculum materials were being tested, and suggested to Miss Mitchell that she invite the current Chairman of the School Health Council, Dick Turner, Head of the Health and Physical Education Department.

On Thursday, when the six of them gathered around the big table in Dr. Herzog's office, there was a feeling of tension even though the usual social amenities were observed. Mr. White introduced Miss Jarvis as their group's public education chairman.

Dr. Herzog opened the meeting. "We're here today at the request of Mr. White, a member of a local health food organization. As I understand it, Mr. White, you are concerned about our school health education program. Would you express your feelings to this group to open our discussion?"

Without hesitation, Mr. White began, "I don't know how you school people can be taken in so easily by the A.M.A. and some of the other groups that are out to control kids' minds. But apparently that's just what has happened here in North Bend. We know for a fact, and Miss Jarvis can corroborate this, that the sixth graders are being indoctrinated in the A.M.A. point of view about foods. Your teachers are using their pamphlets and other materials that follow the same general line, and the North Bend children are not getting scientific information about nutrition and health.

"It's probably not the fault of the teachers, because I understand they don't know much about foods at all — they just say and do what is suggested to them by someone else. And it's easy to fall for the stuff that the medical groups heap on the schools. But to send kids out into the city to question storekeepers, to challenge their integrity and to judge their products on the basis of some biased criteria is simply going too far. The public schools are supposed to present the truth, and they simply aren't doing it here. This kind of literature is humbug," he said as he tossed a pamphlet on the table.

"And I know it's what you're using in school, and it shouldn't be allowed. We're here to protest it. And Miss Jarvis can give you plenty of information about what one of these teachers is really doing — tell them, Bev."

"I visited Miss Starr the other afternoon to get some material for our Health News," Miss Jarvis began. "She told me, without batting an eyelash, that a group of her sixth graders had actually gone to a number of food stores, with her blessing, mind you, to collect information about food products. Then, these kids tried to 'evaluate' the items on the basis of some questions that are pure hokum when it comes to diet foods. The kids finish up this course with a lot of false ideas about natural foods — I know, because Miss Starr gave me that pamphlet herself. She also said she had some extras that she didn't need."

Miss Mitchell, rembering Jeanette Starr's excitement when she told her about the reporter who visited her after school the week before, realized that the reporter was Miss Jarvis. Dr. Herzog was saying, "Perhaps Miss Mitchell would like to respond to these remarks first. Would you, Edith?"

"Yes, I would like to explain how our health education curriculum group goes about its planning. We do have a basic teaching guide, a part of the experimental study, but it is broad and includes much more material than we could ever cover in school. So we have to select priorities, and we decided on two or three major topics for this year, one of which was 'Spending the Food Dollar Wisely.' We wanted to include something about food value, as well as to develop some understandings of how to stay well.

"As always, we got a wealth of materials from just about everywhere — advertising as well as professional publications. Our curriculum group, which includes teachers from several grade levels, examines the material, evaluates it and decides upon its value for our program. This all depends upon its objectives, its vocabulary, accuracy, timeliness and lots of other things. Many materials are unacceptable, and for a variety of reasons. Often, it is simply because they have nothing to add, are repetitious or unsuitable. Sometimes we call on professional help to judge the accuracy of the content. In the case of foods, we consult with our school dietician and also with the people at the Department of Health. We really try to become as knowledgeable as possible in order to help the boys and girls learn.

"As I think I explained before, we believe in developing children's abilities to think critically, so our teachers do their best to help children discover things for themselves — through looking, asking questions, making field trips, organizing information. Our children have been busy doing just that. I don't doubt that they came to your store, Mr. White, but do you object to that as a way to learn about food products?"

"Yes, because you people poison their thinking before they come," he retorted. "Their minds were closed. They picked up every piece of literature in the place and then left. You could tell that someone had sent them out for some purpose. How could they learn anything when they had been told what to think before they came?"

Dr. Herzog asked calmly, "What do you and Mrs. Jarvis think the schools should do?"

"That's simple. Since you aren't giving the true picture about foods and health, you should take health education out of the curriculum entirely. It doesn't belong there anyway. You have plenty of other things to teach."

"But it does belong in the curriculum," Dick Turner, the Chairman of the School Health Council, spoke up. "Health happens to be one of the primary goals of education, and if you don't teach about it, you're neglecting your responsibility. You can certainly appreciate the importance of teaching people how to live in such a way as to conserve and enhance their health, can't you? That's one of our major concerns, and I don't see how you could fail to appreciate its value."

"It is *what* is being taught that we are challenging," Mr. White retorted. "You are giving misinformation. You're not improving children's health by brain-washing them with those false notions about foods. And if you are not going to give them the truth, then health doesn't belong in the schools at all."

"Mr. White, what would your organization like to have about nutrition in our health education curriculum? Do you have materials you would like to have considered along with the others?" Miss Mitchell asked.

"We surely do, and good ones, that give the true facts about what these chemical fertilizers are doing to all of us through what we eat. We have a committee too including some prominent physicians who can attest to their accuracy. No member of your faculty has ever asked us for our materials. All they do is send kids into our stores to snatch what they can."

Dr. Herzog asked, "How would you feel about presenting your materials to the health education curriculum committee for review?"

"We'll be glad to supply enough so that every child can have his own. Even so, I am not sure whether this will be enough to counteract the falsehoods they've been exposed to."

"Now wait a minute," the Assistant Superintendent replied. "I didn't mean to suggest that we would give these materials to every child. I was suggesting that you let the curriculum committee review sample copies and evaluate them, just as they do all others, and decide what might be used."

"Oh, no." Mr. White said. "That committee is not competent to judge them — they haven't studied the subject enough — and they will go right on using the same stuff they are handing out now, thanks to the A.M.A. and its public relations program. As long as the schools won't present the true facts, we want health to be taken out of the curriculum. We know it is unethical, perhaps even illegal, for schools to disseminate one-sided information that can't be proven. And if we don't get satisfaction, we intend to go right to the Board of Education. There is one member, at least, who appreciates the problem and will support our cause. Whether or not you realize it, this is a most important matter. You're leading young people into false beliefs about natural foods and natural healing powers, and what's more, you're doing it all in the name of health!"

Dr. Herzog said, "I'm sorry, Mr. White, but I don't see why your materials should be considered any differently than the others. We regret that the availability of your materials was not brought to our attention when the course was started, but we would still be happy to have our committee review them for possible use in connection with this unit. I hope that you and your organization will think this over and realize that our position is reasonable and fair."

At this point Mr. White and Miss Jarvis got up and left the meeting, obviously dissatisfied with the outcome. Mr. White's last words were, "You'll hear more from us."

As he went out of the door Miss Mitchell slumped back in her chair, looked at Dr. Herzog and asked, "Well, what do we do now?"

"Just sit tight," he answered. "Let's see what happens in the next few days."

A few days later, Dr. Herzog telephoned Miss Mitchell and said, "Edith, I guess the fat is in the fire. I just got a call from the boss to say that the food group has asked for a session with the Board. He's

putting it on the agenda for next Thursday. I must say
he's not very pleased to have any controversy at this
time, even though he feels that we're perfectly right in
the stand we've taken. He's concerned, of course, about
the attendant publicity in view of the forthcoming bond
issue we've worked on so hard for the past year. He
has also received a call from one of our Board members, William Reed, who is apparently supporting this
group's efforts and wanted to be sure the Board would
hear the complaint about health education. I think you
had better plan on being present at the Board meeting.
Maybe you had better ask Dick Turner to come along,
too. Oh, and one more thing, the boss has asked me to
be sure that there's a tape recorder available for the
meeting."

DISCUSSION QUESTIONS

1. Comment on the new approach to health educa-
    tion as described in this case.

2. What are the advantages and disadvantages of
    utilizing community resources in connection with
    education programs?

3. Should teachers like Mary Hall and Jeanette Starr,
    who have had limited preparation in health educa-
    tion, be expected to teach the subject?

4. Should controversial issues like this one be eliminat-
    ed from the school curriculum at the elementary
    level? The secondary level?

5. If Miss Mitchell had been aware of the health food
    group in town and had alerted the teachers, do
    you think they would have handled the subject
    differently? If so, how?

6. Comment on Miss Gibbons' reaction to the
    presentation at the Teachers Institute. Compare the

tactics of her organization with those of any other "pressure groups" you know about in your own community.

7. What community organizations do you think might support the health education curriculum as it exists in North Bend?

8. Discuss the pitfalls of giving information to the press. What should be school policy concerning giving information for publication?

9. Do you think the school health council served any worthwhile purpose?

10. Discuss the meeting between the school personnel and the representatives of the health food group with respect to the presentation of nutrition education in schools.

11. How and by whom should materials be evaluated for their use in schools?

12. Comment on the attitude of the Assistant Superintendent and the Superintendent toward the emerging problem.

13. Do you think this question should properly come before the Board of Education?

14. If you were Miss Mitchell, what would you do prior to the Board of Education meeting?

Selected References

The School Health Issue: Food Fads And Curriculum Content.

American Association for Health, Physical Education and Recreation: *Education for Consumer Health.* Washington, D.C., The Association, 1965, 24 pp.

American Association for Health, Physical Education and Recreation: *Teaching Nutrition in the Elementary School.* Washington, D.C. The Association, 1959.

American Medical Association: *Defenses Against Quackery, A Teacher's Guide Kit.* Chicago, The Association, 1965.

Bauer, W.W.: Education — A Weapon Against Quackery? J. School Health, *34*: 1, 1964.

Byrd, Oliver E.: *School Health Administration*, Philadelphia, W.B. Saunders Co., 1964. (Chapter V. School Health Law).

Council on Foods and Nutrition: Your Campaign Kit to Combat Food Faddism and False Claims, Chicago, American Medical Association, 1959.

Fodor, J.T.: *The Legal Basis for School Health Education in California.* Los Angeles, Brewster Publications, 1962.

Grout R.E.: *Health Teaching in Schools*, 4th Ed., Philadelphia, W.B. Saunders Co., 1963.

Hein, Fred V.: Educational Defenses Against Quackery, J. School Health, *34*: 97, 1964.

Janssen, Wallace F.: The Teacher Versus Quackery in Medicine, J. School Health, *25*: 15, 16, 37, 1954.

Janssen, Wallace F.: The Teacher Versus Quackery in Nutrition, J. School Health, *25*: 21, 27-28, 1954.

Joint Committee on Health Problems in Education of the National Education Association and the American Medical Association: Why Health Education? Washington, D.C., Chicago, The Associations, 1965.

Larimore, G.W.: Educational Resources Against Quackery: Public Health, J. School Health. *35*: 404, 1964.

Martin, Ethel A.: *Nutrition Education in Action*, Rev. Ed., New York, Holt, Rinehart and Winston, 1965.

Mico, Paul R.: The Educational Approach to the Question of Quackery, J. School Health, *34*: 106-111, 1964.

Stare, Frederick J.: Boston Nutrition Society, Plaintiff vs. Frederick J. Stare, Defendant, J. A. M. A., May 25, 1963, pp. 635-639. (A court case involving a nutrition organization on soil infertility and natural foods.)

Teaching Controversial Issues in Health Education, JOHPER Oct. 1961.

Trawick, James L.: Health Education vs. Medical Quackery, J. School Health, *36*: 28, 29, 1965.

Pressure Groups

Adler, Irving: *What We Want From Our Schools*, New York, John Day Co., 1957. (Chapter VIII. The Critics of Progressive Education)

Cressman, George R. and Benda, Harold W.: *Public Education in America — a First Course*. New York, Appleton-Century-Crofts, 1956, pp. 442-446. (The Attacks on the Quality of Education.)

French, Will, Hull, J. Dan and Dodds, B.L.: *American High School Administration Policy and practice*, New York, Rinehart & Co., 1957, *The Anatomy of a Community*, pp. 588-591.

Kimbrough, Ralph: *Political Power and Education Dicision Making*, Chicago, Rand McNally, 1964, pp. 274-275.

Raywid, Mary Anne: *The Ax-Grinders: Critics of our Public Schools*. New York, The Macmillan Co., 1962.

Scott, C. Winfield and Hill, Clyde M. (Ed.): *Public Education Under Criticism*. Englewood Cliffs, N.J., Prentice-Hall, 1954.

Willett, Henry I.: Public Schools Under Pressure, Atlantic, 57-62, Oct. 1954.

Related Background Reading

Bernard, V.: Why People Become the Victims of Medical Quackery. Amer. J. Public Health, 39, Aug, 1965.

Consumers All, Yearbook of the U.S. Department of Agriculture, Washington, D.C., Superintendent of Documents, 1965.

Cooley, Donald: *Beware of Health Quacks*, New York, Berk & Co., 1962.

Deutsch, Ronald M.: *The Nuts Among the Berries*, New York, Ballantine Books, 1961. (Information about food fads and scientific facts about nutrition.)

Health Quackery, a joint publication of the Departments of Health Education and Investigation of the American Medical Association, Chicago, The Association, 1966, 16 pp.

Janssen, Wallace F.: Quackery Can Kill, J. School Health, *25*: 17-18, 42, 1954.

Holbrook, Steward H.: *The Golden Age of Quackery*, New York, The Macmillan Co., 1959, 302 pp.

Johns, E.B.: The Concept Approach in Health Education, J. School Health, *35*: 196-207, 1965.

Kursh, Harry: Mail Order Quacks' Harvest: Dollars and Death, Today's Health, *39*: 30-31, 83-87, 1961.

Smith, Ralph Lee: The Bunk about Health Foods, Today's Health, *43*: 26-30, 1965.

The Health Hucksters, New York, Crowell, 1965.

Stare, Frederick J.: Sense and Nonsense about Nutrition, Harper's Magazine, 66-70, October, 1964.

White, Philip L.: The Food Fanatic's Four Myths of Nutrition, Today's Health, *41*: 72, 1963.

Organizational References

American Association for Health, Physical Education and Recreation, 1201 16th St., N.W., Washington, D.C. 20006.

American Medical Association, 535 North Dearborn St., Chicago, Ill. 60610

Food and Nutrition Board of the National Research Council, Washington, D.C., 20025

National School Public Relations Association, 1201 16th St., N.W. Washington, D.C. 20006

U.S. Department of Health, Education and Welfare, Washington, D.C. 20025. (Children's Bureau, Office of Education, Public Health Service).

School Health Services

4

Just For Kicks

An alarming increase in the illegal use of drugs by young people in a suburban community motivates a school superinten-dent to consider an unusual approach to the problem.

AS he called the meeting of the Advisory Committee on Delinquency to order, Dr. Alfred Johnson, Superin-tendent of the Leesville Schools, told the other ten persons who had assembled, "I appreciate your coming here this evening on such short notice. I would not have called you together like this if there were not a problem of some urgency which I think requires our immediate consideration. But, before I give you the details, I would like to introduce the two gentlemen beside me. On my right is Captain James Meyer, Chief of our county police force, and next to him is Mr. Arthur McGraw, a federal narcotics agent who works in our area. I know these men will be very helpful to us and I am grateful to them for joining us tonight.

"As background information for our two visitors, I want to explain that this Advisory Committee was organized about two years ago. At that time we had been experiencing an increase in delinquency, especially vandalism, and I felt that a group of leaders from the community could give our school personnel some valuable help in dealing with these problems.

"During the couple of years we've been in existence, we've had five or six meetings in which we've tried to get at the roots of these acts of delinquency and to make suggestions about dealing with them.

"Of course, we all know that the problems we are facing here in Leesville are similar to those of our neighboring communities, and we're convinced that one of the contributing factors is simply the phenomenal population growth in all of suburbia. It's hard to believe that only ten years ago we had fewer than 500 children in the entire school district. Today we are approaching 20,000, most of them from families that have moved out of the city in search of better schools. This continuing influx of new families has pressed us into rather rapid expansion. We have had to build new schools and community facilities, to hire more personnel and to increase our services. On the whole, I think we have been successful in keeping up with the growth, and there seems to be a good deal of community pride in our accomplishments. So, it came as a shock to most of us when we began to experience this wanton vandalism and other delinquent behavior by our youngsters.

"I am not referring to occasional pranks that might be attributed to growing kids' temporary rebellious impulses, but to serious anti-social acts that were increasing in number and in costly destruction of property. In my office we received, and continue to receive, many complaints about petty thievery, trespassing, unruly behavior, as well as vandalism. Our local merchants, especially those near the schools, are deeply concerned about some of our students who shoplift. It seems to be a game with these kids to see who can get out of a store undetected with the most merchandise. And this includes girls, too.

"In the schools, our breakage costs for replacement of broken windows has increased steadily, and just last month someone broke into one of our elementary schools and did enough damage to necessitate the closing of the school for an entire day. These are the kinds of problems that this committee is trying to cope with. We have had only limited success to date, but feel that we have taken some very constructive steps that should eventually improve the situation.

"We have tried to tap a variety of resources in our approach to the problem. The Student Council has given us some valuable help by suggesting recreational activities that might provide the fun and adventure young people want. And several of the community agencies have initiated new teen-age programs on the basis of these suggestions. The PTA has had speakers on 'Understanding Adolescents,' and our civic organizations, along with the local newspaper, have supported community pride campaigns. All of these things have been worthwhile.

"While we have been forced to deal with 'problem' children, we've tried to keep a proper perspective on the situation, recognizing that the vast majority of our students do not engage in such destructive behavior and should not be condemned for the comparatively small percentage of students who are responsible.

"Now, the reason that I called this meeting tonight relates to the misuse of drugs — that is why I have asked Captain Meyer and Mr. McGraw to join us. What has happened is this. A few months ago we discovered that some of our high school students who had been suspected of vandalism were carrying quantities of brightly colored capsules. The kids called them pep pills and, when questioned about them, said they got them either from friends, their home medicine cabinet or purchased them in drug stores. They took them just to get a 'high' feeling, they told us.

"We reported these instances to their parents and hoped that they would deal with the situation. But this has not worked out satisfactorily, because many of the same students were discovered to have pills in their possession even after their parents had been alerted.

"About two weeks ago, you probably read in the newspapers about the party over in Maplewood which was raided by the police. Quantities of pills — goof balls, as the users called them — as well as marijuana and heroin were discovered there, and a number of arrests were made. Among the participants were several of our former Leesville High School students — three who dropped out last spring in their junior year. Most of those at the party ranged in age from 19 to 23, and only a few were still enrolled in school. The Leesville boys were taken into police custody and then released to their parents. As I understand it, charges will not be brought against the three boys because they are all under 18 years of age. The others will be brought to trial.

"During the past two weeks our schools have been besieged by telephone calls and letters asking what we are doing about the situation. There have been numerous rumors which have magnified the problem and make it appear that many of our high school students are using narcotics and are likely candidates for dope addiction. Last Friday when a reporter from The Press called, we issued a statement that 'to our knowledge no serious problem of student drug usage exists in Leesville.' I am personally convinced that the number of narcotics users to be found among our student population is insignificant. However, I think this is the time for this committee to consider the matter and suggest what we can do to remedy the existing confusion and prevent further problems of this nature. I am hoping that before we adjourn tonight we will have some specific proposals for action to help stem the illegal use of drugs in our town. Since all of you are leaders of important community groups, I am confident that you will have some practical ideas about involving your organizations in any program we decide to undertake.

"Before we get into a general discussion, I'd like to ask Captain Meyer and Mr. McGraw to give us some basic information about the narcotics problem from the law enforcement point of view. Oh, yes, I have asked my secretary to take some notes for our future guidance, but I want to assure you that our discussion here is confidential and there will be no information released to the press. Mr. McGraw, may we hear from you first?"

"Thank you for inviting me to attend this meeting," the narcotics agent began. "I want to commend all of you for taking such a constructive approach toward narcotics control. If it makes you feel any better, let me assure you that yours is not the only town in the metropolitan area which is faced with a similar problem.

"First, let me remind you that I am an employee of the Bureau of Narcotics, which is a subdivsion of the U.S. Treasury Department. My main function is to investigate and detect violations of narcotics and related laws. These laws date back to 1914 when Congress passed the Harrison Narcotics Act which prohibits the sale, purchase, and possession of narcotics except on a physician's written prescription, and forbids the refilling of a prescription except by written order from the physician.

"In 1951, Congress passed the Boggs Act which includes specific regulations concerning the use of marijuana — the possession of just one marijuana cigarette, for example, is punishable, and even physicians may not possess or prescribe the drug.

"Since 1951, the whole question of drug abuse has been complicated by the appearance of numerous stimulants and depressants in the form of pills which are in wide legal use. For instance, some of us have had our own doctors prescribe one or another of these drugs when they were needed. This is, of course, legal. But there has also been a growing use of these drugs illegally — without a physician's prescription. I would like to emphasize the fact that their ready availability has made it almost impossible to control such illegal use.

These pills are obtained directly by forged prescriptions. In addition, there are pushers who get supplies through black market channels or some other illegal means. Believe me, ladies and gentlemen, where there is a demand, there will always be a supply. And the demand has been growing. From what I know of this area, your main problem with young people is with these pills. The use of marijuana and of heroin is not a serious problem in school age children here at this time, but that doesn't mean it will not become so. The problem, of course, is not only the effects of these pills on those who take them, but also the users' possible graduation into other addicting substances once the kick from the pills seems to be too tame. Persons addicted to heroin have a very bleak future. There are almost no cures at present. And drug addicts are a social menace since they almost certainly must turn to crime to support their habits.

"My primary job as a federal agent is to detect the sources of supply. Usually it is left to local law enforcement agencies to handle the crimes associated with possession and use of drugs and their attendant criminal acts, especially theft and vandalism. In other words, my main job is to cut off the source of the drugs. In this area most of the drugs are obtained from small pushers in the city with little difficulty. We concentrate our efforts on catching the big dealers — those who smuggle the drugs into this country. My department, of course, cooperates with local law enforcement officers whenever called upon. Captain Meyer will probably explain this further. And, if you have any questions later, I'll be glad to answer them."

As Mr. McGraw took his seat, Captain James Meyer, Chief of the County Police, rose and addressed the group. "Mr. McGraw has given you a good explanation of how federal agents work to cut off the source of supply of narcotics into the country. Let me give you some data about our own county.

"During the past 20 years, the county has almost tripled in population. Most of our incoming residents not only come from the city, but return there daily for their work. We often hear our county referred to as a bedroom community because of our large number of commuters, many of whom choose to live here to escape the ills of the city. But, since it is only one hour *to* the city, it is also only one hour *from* the city. So, people who think they are removed from city problems here in Leesville are beginning to find out that they are deluding themselves. As far as drugs are concerned, we are very close to the sources of supply. Though we do not yet have a major problem, it is a growing one, and we want to keep it in check.

"Whereas Mr. McGraw's primary interest is in cutting off the sources of supply, we in the Police Department are concerned with preventing people from getting and using illegal drugs and, of course, with apprehending addicts and getting them under treatment with the slim hope that they can be cured. We are convinced that the only way we can hope to control the number of new users is by removing peddlers of illegal drugs and addicts from society. It is usually the addict who introduces drugs to non-users, and thus is the agent of infection.

"Currently our main problem is with a group who have left high school and who, for one reason or another, have turned to some form of drug as a solution to their own personal problems. These young people often induce others to try drugs 'for kicks' and some high school students are easy prey. They are willing to try amphetamines, barbiturates or marijuana, for instance, and then find it easy to follow the leader in trying other drugs in the search for bigger kicks. And they may end up on heroin. The kids who are becoming involved in this find drug usage a status symbol. They feel like 'big shots'.

"I should also add that the affluence of today's society contributes to the increasing use of illegal drugs. Leesville is not a rich community, but most people who live here are comfortably fixed, and most young people receive adequate allowances. Thus, the expense of the drugs is not an important deterrent initially. It is only after they become addicted and require bigger doses that they have trouble supporting the cost of an expensive habit. That's when you have the increase in theft, breaking and entering, shoplifting, etc.

"The party that was raided a couple of weeks ago did not occur in Leesville, as all of us know. But the boundaries between Leesville and the other adjoining towns are only boundaries in name. What happened in Maplewood could just as easily happen here, and that's why the situation must concern all of us. We in the county Police Department are anxious to help communities and schools.

"Actually, we have given considerable thought to the best plan of action. We believe in a widespread information program and we have men on our force who speak to school groups, usually in assembly programs, and tell them of their first-hand experiences with drug addicts and attempt to give them a picture of the horrible consequences of the addict's way of life. We have some gruesome films that show addicts in the process of withdrawal. We can also display the paraphernalia used by addicts, and we have samples of the pills and other substances. After one of these talks, no one can say that he has not been warned about the dangers of the colorful capsules, the homemade cigarettes and other illegal drugs. We make it a point, too, to tell our audiences what terminology the pushers and addicts use. These talks are very candid and complete in order to make everyone fully aware of the danger of trying a drug even once.

"But, ladies and gentlemen, there are some people who question this approach. They feel that such complete exposure of the facts with detailed descriptions about drug usage merely makes youngsters more curious. In fact, some have accused us of putting ideas into the minds of young people who had no previous awareness of drugs. And they claim, further, that finding out about drugs just makes youngsters want to find out for themselves through experimentation. We don't know the answer, but we think it is better for people to know the facts — in time to do some good.

"Let me conclude by saying that our department is most anxious to work with you in any way we can. Thank you."

As Captain Meyer concluded his remarks, Dr. Johnson said, "Thanks to both of you gentlemen for your enlightening remarks. Captain Meyer, we can well appreciate the dilemma of deciding how much information on narcotics should be given to youngsters. Our teachers face the same problem. Now I think we're ready for questions and comments. I see you're rather anxious to get into this, Mrs. Schwartz."

"I sure am," the President of the High School PTA said. "My telephone hasn't stopped ringing since the Maplewood affair and most callers ask, 'Why aren't the schools doing something about this?' Frankly, I don't know what to tell them."

"Maybe I can throw some light on that," Mr. Parks, Prncipal of the High School replied. "We are mandated by the State to teach about the harmful effects of narcotics, so it's not really a question of *if* we should include the topic in the curriculum, but rather one of *how* to make it an effective educational effort. In view of the comments made here tonight, the question naturally arises as to whether our instruction has been successful.

"We teach about narcotics in our high school biology

and health classes. Usually, one of these subjects is taken by every student during the sophomore or junior year, so that we reach virtually every student attending our high school. We have a course outline that our teachers follow with minor individual variations. Currently we are in the process of reviewing these teaching units to see if they can be improved. Up to this point we have not utilized any of the audio-visual materials on this subject suggested by our guests, but we are giving serious thought to them. Films and other teaching aids will, of course, be previewed by our teachers to determine what to use and how to use it best. From our point of view, we do not feel that an exposure to the facts should have a negative effect on student behavior. With the increasing availability of narcotics, we believe students should learn all the facts from the school rather than from the street corner. If we tell them everything they want to know — including how drugs are used — we think they will be less curious, and certainly more aware of the potential danger of even a little experimentation. We know we can't be 100% effective, but we are convinced that it is better to face up to the problem than to treat it as a hush hush topic or pretend that it couldn't exist in our community."

Mr. Gordon, Chairman of the Little League Association, shook his head and commented, "That's all well and good for those teen-agers, but I think you're starting much too late. It seems to me that something ought to be done earlier — lots earlier."

"You're right," answered Mr. Higgins, Principal of the Southeast Junior High School. "Mr. Barton, my counterpart over at North Junior High and I have discussed this many times, and we agree that high school is too late. We are convinced of the importance of an education program about narcotics at our level, and the only question is what is the most effective approach.

"We, too, are mandated by the State Education

Department to include a unit on narcotics in our General Science classes, but in some respects our problems of presentation are much more difficult than they are in the senior high school. After all, we are dealing primarily with 12, 13 and 14 year olds who have a high level of curiosity and a real desire to find out things for themselves. We encourage them, as a part of the education process, to seek information and arrive at conclusions on their own. So there may be some danger in teaching about drugs. This is one instance where we don't want experimentation and self-discovery!

"We have been concentrating on the beneficial uses of drugs under medical supervision and the dangers of using drugs when they are not prescribed. We aren't sure we're doing enough, and we're currently engaged in some self-evaluation of our curriculum. The teachers at both junior and senior high levels are meeting together regularly now to develop new teaching plans and to consider the utilization of community resources, like the police department."

"That's not early enough," Mr. Gordon replied. "If I had my way about it, the schools would do something about this even earlier. In my opinion...."

"Now let's be reasonable," interrupted Mrs. Schwartz. "Where do the parents fit into this? They have some responsibility too. The schools can't be expected to do it all. Most parents need to be informed about the nature of the problem and particularly about what they should be doing to influence their own children. I've had an earful from some of our mothers of teen-agers, I can tell you. People whom I never heard of before are wondering what the PTA can do to rectify this situation. They're worried about their own kids getting in with the wrong crowd. If it weren't so serious, I'd find it quite amusing because many of these callers haven't been near a PTA meeting in years. Suddenly they are beginning to wake up and take an interest."

"One thing is certain: if we have a PTA meeting on narcotics now, we will have to hang out the Standing Room Only sign. Do you know that we had a meeting on this topic three years ago, and I don't believe we had more than 40 people present, and about half of them were teachers! There just wasn't much interest. In the five years that we've lived in this community and been active in PTA work, the thing that really disturbs me is the general complacency of people — even my own friends and neighbors. It takes a lot to get them to take an interest in the organization that can really do things for their own children. Yes, right now we could get a big turn-out for a one-shot speech on narcotics. But I don't know whether this would really help solve our problem. So many parents seem to dodge responsibility — they'd rather blame the situation on the schools, the neighboring communities or anything else. It is never *their* kids who are the problems — only other people's kids. You should have seen the PTA attendance the night we had a psychiatrist talk on 'What's Wrong With Your Neighbor's Children?' "

Mrs. Schwartz's comments brought a few chuckles from the group and then Richard Eldridge, Director of Pupil Personnel Services spoke up. "Let me start by saying that it would *appear* that we have no problem with our students. It's true, we all know about that party over in Maplewood which did include some boys from our town, but those boys aren't in school. And if you looked through our health records and counselors' reports, you wouldn't find anything about drugs. And that's why I say *apparently* we have no problem. But I know this is not a true picture.

"The fact is that Captain Meyer has talked with me several times about young people in our schools who are suspected of using narcotics, or who have had minor brushes with the law on other counts and admitted to having used narcotics at least once. From the figures that he has given me and the cases I have investigated during the past year, I would guess that we must have at least 75 young people using some form of drugs, either occasionally or regularly.

"Now, 75 may not sound like a very large figure in a system of our size, but when you analyze it, you realize that it is close to 5% of our junior and senior high school population. And that, you can be sure, is a problem, especially since the use of narcotics can be expected to spread, like an infectious disease. And the spread is what we are most alarmed about.

"The question must arise in your minds as it has in mine: why is it that we school people did not discover these young people first? After all, there are required periodic health examinations. More than that, many, though not all, of these users are the under-achieving students who have been referred to our guidance counselors. And yet, none has ever mentioned using drugs or knowing others who do. And even when asked directly, not one has ever admitted to a counselor or a nurse that he has experimented with narcotics. One reason that this information has never appeared on a health record might be explained by the fact that over 80% of our students have their annual checkups by their own doctors who check off the health record forms and mail them in. Sometimes I suspect that the physicians may not have seen the students at all, but merely filled out the forms to do the parents a favor.

"Well, whatever the reason or reasons, we now know that there is a problem, that it is growing, and that we must find some way of heading it off before it becomes really serious. I don't have a specific sugges-tion right now, other than to try to help teachers and parents develop a greater sensitivity to the signs that might indicate a drug problem."

When Eldridge finished speaking, there was silence for a moment, and then Bernard Malcolm spoke up, obviously trying to control his anger. "I'm convinced that there *are* things that can be done to stop this narcotics business right now, and I may not be popular when I say that a lot of what is needed around Leesville is some good firm disciplining of children, especially teen-agers. Parents and school authorities need to be much more stern in correcting the loose behavior that seems to have been adopted by young people today. They want freedom. They want independence. And they get it — from their parents and from the school. But they just don't know how to handle it. And I, for one, think it is a bad thing.

"Now you all know the group I represent, Rotary, is composed of many of our leading business and professional men, all of whom are interested in making Leesville a good place in which to live and work. Since all of our members earn their living right here in town, they know what's going on, and they're disturbed by the attitudes of some of our teen-agers. Some of our members have had to order these teen-agers out of their places of business because they are so disruptive — to say nothing of the stealing. I can't speak for all the Rotarians, but I think most of them agree with me that this is the direct result of lack of training both in the home and at school.

"If you need further evidence, you should see some of the teen-age parties that are going on. Just the other night there was a party held in the home of one of the young girls who lives down the block from me. I was aghast at the noise and the lewd language. The next morning there were enough beer cans in front of that house to fill two garbage pails. I'm not even sure whether the parents were there or not, but, these kids need supervision and discipline. They are just the ones who will try anything — legal or illegal — just for the excitement of seeing whether they can get away with it.

"In short, I think there are just two things that

need to be done to nip all these problems right now. One, strict law enforcement — especially arresting those outsiders who come into Leesville and hang around where they might try to sell drugs to our young people — and two, a tightening up of discipline in the schools and in homes."

Father Oliver Miller, a member of the Inter-denominational Ministerial Association, was the next person to speak. "I wish it were as simple as that, Mr. Malcolm. But, I'm afraid you're treating symptoms rather than causes. All of my colleagues are very much concerned with the problems confronting this community. We talked about it just last week after Dr. Johnson had asked that someone from our group attend this meeting, and I hope I can give you the gist of our thinking.

"Of course, we're all disturbed about these recent developments, but we have been aware of the ferment and confusion in the minds of our adolescents for quite some time. You will recall that when this Committee began to discuss delinquency problems a couple of years ago, the churches and synagogues embarked on an expanded teen-age recreation program, for the express purpose of providing a wholesome climate where young people might engage in social activities. My colleagues and I are convinced that this has been of some help, but obviously there is a great deal more that must be done. Evidently, we are not reaching those young people who are participating in acts which are not desirable and are actually harmful. None of our youth organizations have even discussed the current drug problem. Maybe we should encourage such discussion.

"We believe that parents need to be involved more than they are in the activities of their children. In our religious organizations we have the same difficulties that Mrs. Schwartz reports concerning the PTA. It is hard to get the parents to participate, though they are glad to have their children attend. This is something we all have to deal with.

"Our ministerial council talked about what we could do, both individually and collectively, and we are agreed that we cannot sit by idly. Obviously, our approach will have to be much more fundamental than pointing out the effects of narcotics addiction. Basically, this is a question of moral and spiritual values, and that is what makes the churches most important. The schools can't possibly deal with this adequately. Though I have nothing concrete to report, you can rest assured that we will do everything in our power to help solve this particular problem, but we must look upon it as a part of a much bigger concern, which is the lack of influence of the church and the home on our young people."

"Thank you, Father Miller," Dr. Johnson said. "Now we have one other person who would like to air his views on the subject. You all know our Board of Education President, Dan Davidson. We are all interested in his comments."

"It has been a long evening," Mr. Davidson said, "and I am not sure there is very much I can add to what has already been said. However, you must be aware that the Board's position in this situation is clearcut. As you know, the Board of Education, whose members are elected representatives of the community, is empowered by law to formulate policy for our School District. You have heard it stated earlier that we are mandated by the State to teach about the harmful effects of drugs and narcotics. This we have done and are doing. But like anything else in the curriculum, the results must be evaluated. It would seem that some new approaches may be in order, and this is the responsibility of our school administration and professional staff to determine. I am confident that Dr. Johnson and his staff will continue to study the situation and try out new methods.

"It would be very easy for your Board of Education to place blame for the narcotics problem on the community itself, or perhaps, on forces outside of the community. After all, schools do not give courses in vandalism and shoplifting, or propound the blissful effects of taking barbiturates, smoking pot or sniffing glue. Yet, these things are going on and we must experiment with new ways to try to provent their occurrence. This our schools will do. And if more money is needed to help combat narcotics use, I am certain that the citizens of Leesville will provide it. But we will be powerless in our efforts unless we can enlist the help of everyone living here. This is a job for the whole town, not the schools alone. I think we should thank Dr. Johnson for calling us all together, Though we don't seem to have arrived at any new program for combatting this menace, I am hopeful that our intensified efforts in the many groups we represent will help to reduce the problem. My thanks also to Mr. Meyer and Mr. McGraw for coming here this evening. I would suggest we meet again two weeks from tonight to see what concrete proposals we can come up with."

As Dr. Johnson was driving Dick Eldridge home, he commented, "I'm glad you didn't have your car tonight, Dick, because I wanted to get your reaction to tonight's meeting anyway. Do you think we made any progress?"

"Oh, of course, even though it may not seem like it. I think it's awfully important to get all segments of the community involved in seeking solutions to this nasty problem, and I'm sure we'll see an upsurge of attention to it.

"But I've given this matter a lot of thought ever since I talked with Bob Parker the other day when he dropped in after the Junior High track meet. I'm so glad we got Bob to join our school system last year. He's really doing a whale of a job with those kids. He and I talked about this narcotics business, and what he told me has set me to thinking about an idea that might really work. Would you have time to hear about it now?"

"Oh, sure," said Dr. Johnson. "I'm so hopped up now — if you'll pardon the expression, that I won't be able to unwind for a while anyway, so go ahead."

"Like I said earlier this evening," Eldridge began, "the hardest job we have is finding out which kids are already using drugs. We couldn't discuss how to do that in a meeting like tonight's, though we did get some helpful suggestions for discouraging youngsters from experimenting with drugs, our Rotary President not-withstanding. But what about those students who are already hooked, or well on the way to becoming so. We want to help them, of course, but more important than that, we want to keep them from getting others to follow the same pattern. That is the way this hideous thing is spread.

"I mentioned that there are 75 suspected users in the schools. I'm not sure that this number is accurate — it might be a conservative figure. But no one, such as myself, who is officially designated as a counselor, is going to have any chance of getting close to these kids and their problems. They won't come to us. Moreover, they won't go to their parents or to the clergy. So, if we want to find out who they are and how we can help them, we need to do it in some 'unofficial' way. And this is where Bob Parker might come in.

"He is the kind of person that kids really like. I guess there is at least one like him in every school system. People like Bob have an indefinable quality which kids sense. They just know that he cares about them and they look upon him more as a friend than a teacher. In other words, they don't see him as a member of the school establishment. They also know that he will not be punitive, and what is most impor-

tant, that he can be trusted. But, put Bob Parker in an
official guidance position, and you reduce his potential
for informally communicating with students. They will
no longer seek him out to discuss their problems because
he has become an authority figure — an arm of the
administration, as it were.

"Bob has told me of a number of kids who have
talked to him about their own and their friends' experiences in trying drugs, and he is beginning to be
bothered about what to do with this information. Since
I was instrumental in bringing Bob to this district, and
we are close personal friends, he came to me for advice.
He wants to help, but the question is how. I would like
to suggest that as long as Bob Parker is willing, that
he be given encouragement and authority to pursue
these narcotics leads that may unearth the sources of
drugs. This would enable him to work with me and
with the narcotics agent and police chief in trying not
only to help the kids already involved, but also to
uncover the source of this infection — the pushers.

"This requires some delicate, tactful handling by
Bob so that his usefulness will not be impaired. No one
should be aware of his assignment, but he would need
to have time to carry it out. He would have to have
a lighter teaching schedule to free him for pursuing
leads and carrying on private conversations with
those students who want to confide in him. If you
agreed with this idea, perhaps it would be possible to
assign him to a recreation job that would require him
to be at the Junior Highs and at the Senior High,
particularly in after-school activities. Then he would be
able to contact more students and learn more about
what is going on. I am convinced that this approach
would have more possibility for success than anything
else that has been suggested tonight. What are your
reactions?"

"You mean, he would be like a school narcotics agent?"

"Well, yes, in a sense. Part of his job would be to seek information about drug usage, to become a confidante of those kids on drugs, in this way finding out the sources of drugs, which then could be cut off by the appropriate agency. And all the time he would hold the official title of Recreation Director."

"I'll have to give it some thought," Dr. Johnson replied, "because it would mean that the Board of Education would have to hire a new teacher to take Bob Parker's Gym classes. Would I take the Board into my confidence, or simply sell the deal on the basis of our need for a better after-school recreation program? Then too, there would be a problem — to whom would Bob Parker report? And, as I think out loud, wouldn't there be some element of risk in what he is doing if he has to get involved with pushers — even those who might be our own students?

"Why don't you and Parker drop in to see me tcmorrow morning so we can talk about it some more?"

DISCUSSION QUESTIONS

1. What is the school's responsibility for detecting and dealing with narcotics users?

2. What is the school's responsibility for education about the use and misuse of drugs?

3. What do you think should be the objectives, the content and the approach to narcotics education in schools? Comment on the program in Leesville.

4. Discuss the pros and cons of using the educational approach described by the Police Chief.

5. Was the Leesville school health service department deficient in not knowing about student drug usage?

6. What are the merits of the plan suggested by Dick Eldridge?

7. What are the drawbacks of the plan?

8. If you were Superintendent Johnson, what would be your reaction to Dick Eldridge's suggestion?

Selected References

The School Health Issue: Drug Abuse and the Schools.

American Association for Health, Physical Education and Recreation: *Drug Abuse: Escape to Nowhere*, Washington, D.C., The Association, 1967, 104 pp.

Anderson, C.L.: *School Health Practice*. 3rd Ed., St. Louis, The C.V. Mosby Co., 1964. (p. 285. School-Community Health Council; p. 371-375. Resource Unit: Tobacco, Alcohol and Drugs.)

Ausubel, David P.: Causes and Types of Narocotic Addiction: A Psychosocial View, Psychiatric Quarterly, *35*: 523, 1961.

Ausubel, David P.: *Drug Addiction: Physiological, Psychological and Sociological Aspects*. New York, Random House, 1958.

Byrd, Oliver: *School Health Administration*. Philadelphia, W.B. Saunders Co., 1964. (Chapter 11. Narcotics Education. Detection of Pupil Addicts.)

California State Department of Education: *Drug Abuse. A Source Book and Guide for Teachers*. Sacramento, 1967. (Includes chapters on instruction about drugs and detection of drug users.)

Facts about Narcotic Drug Addiction, prepared by the National Institute of Mental Health. U.S. Department of Health, Education and Welfare, Public Health Service. Publication No. 1322. Washington, D.C. 20201. 1965. 4 pp.

Harms, Ernest, (Ed.): *Drug Addiction in Youth*. New York, Pergamon Press (Macmillan), 1965.

Prevention and Control of Narcotic Addiction. Bureau of Narcotics, Washington, D.C., U.S. Treasury Dept. 1962.

Proceedings, White House Conference on Narcotic & Drug Abuse, Sept. 27 & 28, 1962. Washington, D.C., U.S. Government Printing Office, 1963.

Radin, Sherwin S.: Psychosocial Aspects of Drug Addiction, J. School Health, *36*: 481-487, 1966.

Saltman, Jules: *What We Can Do About Drug Abuse.* Public Affairs Pamphlet No. 390. New York, Public Affairs Committee, Inc. 10016. 1966.

The President's Advisory Commisson on Narcotic and Drug Abuse: Final Report, Washington, D.C., U.S. Government Printing Office, Nov., 1963.

U.S. Department of Health, Education and Welfare, Public Health Service. The Protection and Promotion of Mental Health in Schools, Mental Health Monograph No. 5, 1966.

Related Background Reading

Adler, Irving: *What We Want For Our Schools.* New York, John Day Co., 1957. (Chapter VI. Moral Values and Juvenile Delinquency).

American Medical Association: Mental Health and School Health Services, Chicago, The Association, 1964, 23 pp.

Bronfenbrenner, Urie: The Split-Level American Family. Saturday Review, 60-66, Oct. 7, 1967.

Bruner, Jerome S: *The Process of Education.* New York, Vintage Books, 1960.

Coleman, James S.: *The Adolescent Society.* New York, The Free Press of Glencoe (Macmillan), 1961.

Downey, Lawrence W.: *The Secondary Phase of Education.* New York, Blaisdell Publishing Co. (Ginn & Co.), 1965. (pp. 137-141, The Informal Group and Sub-Cultural Group).

French, Will, Hull, J. Dan and Dodds, B.L.: *American High School Administration.* New York, Rinehart & Co., 1957. (Chapter 3. Youth Education in our Democratic Society).

Friedenberg, Edgar Z.: *Coming of Age in America.* New York, Random House, 1965.

Glueck, Sheldon and Glueck, Eleanor: *Delinquents in the Making: Paths to Prevention.* New York, Harper Brothers, 1962.

Good, H.G.: *A History of American Education.* New York, The Macmillan Co., 1962. (pp. 546-49, High School Inquiries).

Hand, Harold C.: *Principles of Public Secondary Education.* New York, Harcourt, Brace Co., 1958. (Chapter 5. Improving the Holding Power of the Secondary School.)

Musgrove, F.: *Youth and the Social Order.* Bloomington, Indiana, The University of Indiana Press, 1965.

Nordstrom, Carl, Friedenberg, Edgar Z. and Gold, Hilary A.: *Society's Children: A Study of Resentement in the Secondary School.* New York, Random House, 1967.

Watenberg, William W. (Ed.): *Social Deviancy Among Youth.* Chicago, National Society for the Study of Education, 65th Yearbook, Part 1, 1966.

Wellington, C. Burleigh and Wellington, Jean: *Teaching for Critical Thinking.* New York, McGraw-Hill Book Co., 1960. (pp. 61-68, Developmental Problems).

Organizational References

American Association for Health, Physical Education and Recreation, 1201 16th St., N.W., Washington, D.C. 20006.

American Medical Association, 535 North Dearborn St., Chicago, Ill. 60610

American Social Health Association, 1740 Broadway, New York, N.Y., 10019

National Association for Mental Health, 10 Columbus Circle, New York, N.Y. 10019.

U.S. Department of Health, Education and Welfare. Washington, D.C. 20025. (Children's Bureau, Office of Education, Pubic Health Service).

5

The Root Of
The Problem

To what extent should schools accept responsibility for providing dental treatment for children?

ALTHOUGH it was after six o'clock, there was still daylight as the Clayland High School junior varsity football team finished practice and ran from the field into the locker-room. It was a crisp October day, and the Assistant Coach, John Kelly, was pleased with the way his younger boys had handled themselves in the scrimmage with the varsity team. As he entered the physical education office and saw the Head Coach, Harry McKnight, making some notations at his desk, he said, "If you're not careful, we'll be taking those big lugs of yours for sure. How did you like the way the J.V. played?"

"They were darned good, and you deserve a lot of credit for bringing those boys along so well. I'm not so worried about next year's varsity now, even though I'm losing most of my team because they're graduating. A few more like that Ramirez boy and we've got it made!"

"Yes, how about him?" Kelly replied. "You know, he's only a sophomore. Give him a few more pounds in the right places and a couple more inches, and you'll have one of the sweetest quarterbacks in the county. I got to talking with him, and he's a real nice kid. His family just moved here last summer from the city. You know, Harry, the usual thing. The family got fed up with the city, sunk all their savings in one of those development houses on 2500 square feet of God's almost green earth. Now, both Papa and Mama have to work like mad to make ends meet. He's a factory worker in the city, and I think she's a part time waitress. I believe there are two younger kids besides Jose."

"That's Clayland for you," McKnight said. "I'll bet over half of our population is in the same boat, and the percentage is getting higher all the time. Being the first town outside the city limits, we're sitting ducks for people who get a little wanderlust but can't afford to move far from their jobs. But I'm not complaining. Just keep the Ramirezes coming. I love it."

Shortly after the fall semester, Harry McKnight, as was his practice, checked to find out how his boys were getting along scholastically. He always tried to impress his athletes with the importance of keeping their grades up and was known as a hard taskmaster, both on the football field and in the classroom. Like most of his coaching colleagues, McKnight had a full teaching schedule, in his case, mathematics. Ramirez was one of the students he checked. He located Isobel Cherkasky, the Guidance Counsellor assigned to Jose, and asked her about him.

"Jose is a real student," she said, as she pulled out his record. "I remember him very well. He's got a good mind, uses it, and has a nice manner. I wish all of the 350 assigned to me were like him. Then I wouldn't complain about my load. Jose is definitely college material, but he sure is going to need financial help. The family, although not indigent, needs every penny to maintain a decent standard. But they're the salt-of-the-earth — the kind of people who make you think it's all worthwhile. Don't worry about Jose, he'll do O.K."

"I'm sure glad to hear that. I expect him to be one of our varsity mainstays next year."

The next few months found McKnight completely immersed in his school work, his family life and the two courses he was taking in the city to prepare himself for a possible future administrative position. He was also involved as the director of a summer camp which kept him busy, not only during the summer, but also in the spring, primarily interviewing college students who wanted camp jobs. So, before he knew it, June first had rolled around, and he wanted to talk individually with his football prospects for next fall, especially since they had to report for practice on the first day of school.

When Jose came to his office, the coach was shocked at the boy's appearance. He had not seen him since the preceding fall. The boy had lost weight, and his complexion was sallow. Also the quick-smiling, alert look was missing. "What's wrong, Jose? You almost look as if you're in pain. Have you been sick?"

"I'm O.K., Mr. McKnight. I'm having a little trouble with my teeth, but I'm going to a dentist and he's fixing me up. You'll see, by September I'll be in good shape. You still want me to go out for varsity?"

"I sure do," replied McKnight. "But you'd better take care of yourself so you'll be ready to play. Are you sure you're being taken care of?"

"Oh, yes. The school dentist checked my teeth last month and told me I'd have to see a dentist. Our family doesn't have one, but my father asked our neighbor who to go to and then sent me to their dentist. I gave the dentist the card the school sent home, and he has already signed it and sent it back to Mrs. Chapman, the school nurse. Don't worry, Coach, everything will be O.K. You can count on me for next year. Hope you have a good summer."

McKnight was not pleased with what he had seen, so the next day he dropped in to talk with the school nurse. As soon as she saw him, she exclaimed, "Well, if it isn't the muscle and brawn man. I'll bet you're here to check up on one of your beef-trust!"

"Now look, Mrs. Chapman, don't let your prejudices

show. We've been through this before. I just want to get some information about a boy whose teeth were checked by Dr. Simon during the dental screening last month. His name is Jose Ramirez."

"Ramirez, Ramirez," murmured Mrs. Chapman as she looked through her files. "There must be dozens of them. I don't know what this town is coming to; we never had a name like that when I came here 25 years ago. Oh well, that's progress, I suppose. What did you say his first name is — Jose? Oh yes, here it is. He was checked May first, and he had a large number of carious teeth. In fact, Dr. Simon indicated that his mouth was very bad. We sent a notice home the next day for the family to check with their own dentist. When we didn't get the card back within three weeks, we sent out a reminder notice. That was returned just a few days ago signed by a Dr. Walter Easton, who indicated that the Ramirez boy was being seen by him. Frankly, I'm surprised. In so many cases of this type, we never even get an answer. O.K., Coach?"

McKnight, controlling his annoyance, thanked Mrs. Chapman, thinking to himself, "I must remember to kiss my wife when I get home. As for Jose, all seems to be well."

The opening of school in the fall was, as usual, hectic and demanding, as new classes and extracurricular activities got underway. Coach McKnight's every minute was consumed with planning lessons, checking equipment and uniforms and coaching "his boys" in their first football practices. When Jose did not show up after the squad's second work-out, the Coach became concerned and sent for the boy.

When Jose came into his office, the Coach was again shocked by the boy's appearance. He seemed to have lost more weight, looked fatigued and held his mouth tight-lipped as though he were in pain.

"Jose, how come you haven't been out for practice? What's wrong?"

Jose dropped his eyes and said in a low voice, "I'm sorry, Mr. McKnight, but I think I'd better forget about football this year. I don't think I'd be good enough to make the team anyhow."

"Why not? Are you still having problems with your teeth? I thought you were getting them fixed this summer. You were seeing your dentist when I talked with you last spring. Mrs. Chapman told me you were going-ing to someone, what was his name?"

"Dr. Easton," the boy replied. "I did visit him twice and he filled the cavities. He took some x-ray pictures, or something, and he told me he wanted me to see another dentist — a specialist. So I went over to see this dentist — his name is Dr. Saunders, and he took some more x-ray pictures. He told me I would have to see him once or twice a week for the whole summer for some treatments. I told him I'd think about it. I had a job taking care of some people's lawns and I just never got around to going back."

"Look, Jose, you're not telling me everything. This doesn't sound like you. There must be more to this. I know how anxious you are to go out for the team, and yet you neglected to take care of the only thing that's preventing you from doing so. How come?"

"O.K., Mr. McKnight. I'll level with you. When I saw Dr. Saunders, he told me that if I don't have some special work done on four of my teeth, I'll lose them. He said something about root canal work and that it'll take a long time. I asked him how much it would cost and he said that it would be about $750. Now look, Mr. McKnight, that's a lot of money, and my parents can't afford it. I know that they would try to swing it, somehow, but I just didn't have the heart to tell them. So I decided to let it go for now and try to earn enough money to get it done sometime. And even though I feel lousy and even if I give up football, at least I won't have to add to my parents' troubles with this thing. I already saved up to $78, and I've got an after-school job. Besides if I lost a few teeth, so what? I still have plenty left. Anyway, those four are in the back."

"Jose, let me look into this and see what can be done. I admire what you are trying to do, but somehow, there must be a way to work this out."

"Thanks just the same, Mr. McKnight, but I just don't want my mother and father to know about this. They can't pay for it — I know how strapped they are — and we don't want charity."

Mr. McKnight started to remonstrate with Jose, but thought better of it, and sent him off, telling him to take care of himself.

As soon as the boy left, McKnight put in a call for Dr. Simon, the school dentist. The dentist called back later that afternoon, and McKnight told him of his conversation with Jose. "I would appreciate it very much," the teacher continued, "if you would be kind enough to check with Dr. Easton and Dr. Saunders about Jose. Normally, I wouldn't bother you about this. I realize you are retained by the school system on a part-time basis, and that you'll never be able to retire on what they pay you. But, frankly, if I ask Mrs. Chapman, I might give this whole thing the kiss of death."

Dr. Simon chuckled. "I think I know what you mean. Let me call Easton and Saunders. I know both of them well, and I'll let you know what I find out. The boy sounds like a wonderful kid. I'll get in touch with you in a day or two."

Several days later Dr. Simon called McKnight and told him, "I talked with Dr. Easton, and he pretty much substantiates what Jose told you. The boy had 12 cavities and these were filled. But this was only part of the problem since the x-ray pictures showed that there are four other teeth, all in the lower left jaw, that are in poor shape. The roots of the first and second molars are in bad condition and need treatment, if they are to be saved. And, in addition to those molars, the two bicuspids in the same lower left jaw don't look good, and they need attention too. The fact that these four teeth are all in a row complicates the situation, because of the difficulty of finding a sound tooth to anchor a bridge to if extractions are necessary. That's why it is so important to try to save whatever teeth can be saved. And that's why Easton sent the boy to Saunders.

"Easton received a report from Saunders who, incidentally, is one of two endodontists in this area, and he needs new patients like he needs a hole in the head. What it all boils down to is that either Jose gets endodontic work done immediately, with a good likelihood of saving those teeth, or the tooth should be extracted right now. In that event some extensive bridge work needs to be done since he will, in effect, lose the use of the left side of his mouth, and it could cause him a lot of trouble in the future. This process is costly too. To do it right — fixing it permanently — would probably cost as much as the endodontia, in the neighborhood of seven or eight hundred dollars. Let's face it, Jose's teeth are in such poor condition, that whatever he has done — even extractions and temporary replacements — will cost several hundred dollars. For someone his age, I would strongly recommend that every attempt be made to save the teeth right now while there's still a chance. With the condition of his teeth, I'd suspect he might be in some pain."

"I think he is," said the Coach. "He's probably living on aspirin and guts. Well, I think I have the picture, Dr. Simon. It's either root canal work or extractions with replacements. Either process, however, will be expensive and to Jose, practically out of reach. However, there's much more at stake here than the physical problem. This whole business is having a profound effect on Jose's mental well-being. His grades are apt to be affected, and before long he could become another dropout. I know he could be an outstanding football player, and that plus his ability to get good grades could get him the wherewithal to go on to college. I know some people take a dim view of athletic scholarships, but let me tell you, this kid would be a credit to any college. What I'm afraid of is that his motivation and drive could easily go down the drain because of this dental problem."

"I couldn't agree with you more, McKnight. But I'm afraid that's Jose's problem. Well, maybe I shouldn't put it quite that way. He has you in his corner, and maybe you can help him work something out. Unfortunately, I can't really help. My job with the school is simply to inspect mouths and see that parents of kids needing work are notified. What's done after that is out of my hands. I think you should check with Mrs. Chapman. Maybe she can come up with something."

"I'll sure try, and many thanks for your help."

Two days later, McKnight settled down in a chair in Edith Chapman's office and told her what he had learned about Jose, expressed his feelings about the boy's future and wound up by asking, "Isn't there some way the school can help? Couldn't you find some way of arranging some financial aid? Aren't there some PTA funds — or maybe some community group that could help this kid?"

The Nurse had listened in silence while the Coach talked, but when he posed his final question, she practically leaped from her seat. "I've been waiting for you to suggest something like that! Now you just listen to me, McKnight. I've been here a long time, and I'm not happy with the changes I see around here. Parents expect the school to do everything. It used to be that when a notice was sent home about a child's health, the parents either did something about it, or if they didn't, they wouldn't come to the school begging for help. They understood there was a limit to what a school should be expected to do, and they knew that getting medical or dental treatment for their kids and paying for it was their own responsibility.

"But around here today it's different. People expect to have everything done for them — by government or someone else. The school is expected to do everything for kids from feeding them hot lunches to treating their physical and mental ills. Did I say expected? What I should really say is 'demanded'. Many of these parents — it's really the parents' fault, not the kids — are just as well off as we are. After all, McKnight, we're never going to get rich teaching school. But we are expected to pay our own bills no matter how high they are. And if we don't have the money, then we borrow it. I know. Since my husband died, I've been the sole wage earner in the family and I want to tell you it hasn't been easy to bring up two girls on my salary. Yet somehow I managed, but I don't go around expecting the school, or anyone else, to arrange discounts or free service for me or the girls.

"But you should see the requests for help I get here. Every time I send out any health examination notices asking parents to check on their children, I get a lot of calls or visits to tell me they can't afford to take care of these things themselves and couldn't the school pay for them, or at least, find someone who would do the work for less money? They expect me to make arrangements for everything from fitting eyeglasses to surgery for tonsils or hernias. It would take at least one other full-time nurse if the schools ever took on the job of arranging for diagnosis and treatment of kids' problems, to say nothing of finding some benevolent persons or organizations willing to pay for it. What do they think the schools are running here — a clinic?

"And I'll bet Jose's family makes as much as I do. I am really sorry for Jose and his troubles, but I think he has to tell his parents about them, and they must work out a way for paying for the dental work themselves. What if they do have to borrow money? We can't do it for them. We're running a school, not a welfare agency. The root of this problem is the general attitude of people these days — who forget that schools are for education — not health service."

DISCUSSION QUESTIONS

1. Analyze each character and suggest their motivations.

2. What is the value of the dental health appraisal in schools?

3. What should be the extent of services that schools provide?

4. Should a mathematics teacher be a coach?

5. What do you think of Edith Chapman as a nurse? Compare her with Isobel Cherkasky.

6. Should school dentists be limited to inspections only?

7. What would be the role of a dental hygienist in a situation like this one?

8. Does the income level of the community affect the amount of services a school should offer?

9. To what extent should a PTA or other community group be involved in financing health services?

10. Should a school nurse be expected to make referrals of children who are not on welfare, nor medically indigent?

11. What should be the relationship between private practitioners and the schools?

12. Do private practitioners have any responsibility for keeping the school informed of health care needed or in progress?

13. How do you feel about athletic scholarships?

14. Do you think the coach is as concerned about his mathematics students' health as he was about his football team's?

15. If you were Mrs. Chapman, what would you do now?

16. If you were McKnight, what would you do now?

Selected References

The School Health Issue: The Extent of Health Services.

American Academy of Pediatrics: Report of the Committee on School Health. The Academy, P.O. Box 1034, Evanston, Ill. 60204. 1966. (pp. 17-24, Dental Health and Dental Examination and Follow-Up).

Dollar, Melvin L., and Sandell, Perry J.: Dental Programs in Schools. J. School Health, *31*: 3-14, 1961.

American Dental Association. A Dental Health Program for Schools. Chicago, The Association, 1965.

Anderson, C.L.: *School Health Practice.* 3rd Ed., St. Louis, The C.V. Mosby Co., 1964. (Chap. 7. Appraisal Aspect of Health Services. Chap. 10. Remedial Aspects of Health Services).

Byrd, Oliver E.: *School Health Administration.* Philadelphia, W.B. Saunders Co., 1964. (Chap. 14. The School Nurse. Chap. 23. The School Dental Program.)

Cauffman, Joy G., Petersen, Eleanora S., and Emrick, John A.: Medical Care of School Children: Factors Influencing Outcome of Referral from a School Health Program. Amer. J. Public Health, *57*: 1967.

Field, Doris, Responsibility of the Health Services. J. School Health, *31*: 338-340, 1961.

Gabrielson, Ira W., Levin, Lowell S. and Ellison, Margaret D.: Factors Affecting School Health Follow-up. Amer. J. Public Health. *57*: 1967.

Gutman, Ross E.: The Team-Oriented School Dental Health Program in New York State, J. School Health, *32*: 321-323, 1962.

Haag, Jessie Helen: *School Health Program.* New York, Henry Holt Co., 1958. (Chapter 4. Dental Health. pp. 454-455, Medical Treatment by Public Schools).

Hannah, E. Pearl: Palo Alto's School Dental Health Program. J. School Health, *30*: 268, 1960.

Hardy, Martha C.: Parent Resistance to the Need for Remedial and Preventive Services. J. Pediat. 104, 1956.

Langton, Clair V., Allen, Ross L. and Wexler, Philip: *School Health— Organization and Services,* New York, The Ronald Press, 1961.

Mayshark, Cyrus and Shaw, Donald D.: *Administration of School Health Programs. Its Theory and Practice.* St. Louis, The C.V. Mosby Co., 1967. (pp. 194-198. Dental Examinations.)

Misner, Paul J., Schneider Frederick W., and Keith, Lowell G.: *Elementary School Administration.* Columbus, Ohio, Charles E. Merrill, Books, Inc., 1963. (pp. 304-307. Health Services).

National Committee on School Health Policies of the National Education Association and the American Medical Association. *Suggested School Health Policies.* 4th Ed., Chicago, American Medical Association, 1966. (Chapter 2. School Health Services.)

Nemir, Alma: *The School Health Program,* Philadelphia, W.B. Saunders Co., 1965. (Chapter 7. Problems of Dental Health. Chapter 17. Organization and Administration of the School Health Program.)

Schultz, C.S.: Trends in School Health Service. Amer. J. Public Health, *53*: 1447, 1963.

Smolensky, Jack and Bonvechio, L. Richard: *Principles of School Health.* Boston, D.C. Heath & Co., 1966. (Chapter 5. School Health Services.)

Stoll, Frances A.: Dental Health Inspections in the Schools, J. School Health, *31*: 55, 1961.

Shear, Bruce E.: Dental Health Service in Pupil Personnel Services. J. School Health. *35*: 300-303, 1965.

Truhart, A.H.: Guidelines for Dental Care and Treatment Programs for Children, J. School Health. *33*: 70-75, 1963.

Turner, C.E. and Sellery, C. Morley and Smith, Sara Louise: *School Health and Health Education,* 4th Ed., St. Louis, The C.V. Mosby Co., 1961. (pp. 158-159. Dental Examinations. pp. 133-136. (Dental Defects. pp. 79-92. Duties of Members of the School Health Team.)

Wagner, M.G.: The Medical Basis for School Health Programs, School Review. *69*: 322-337, 1961.

Wallace, Helen M.: Utilization of Private Physicians and Dentists in School Health, J. School Health, *34*: 65-68, 1964.

Wilson, Rebert E.: *Educational Administration*, Columbus, Ohio, Charles E. Merrill Books, Inc., 1966. (pp. 591-2. Service to Pupils' Health Needs).

Nurse in the School Health Program

A National Committee of School Nurses for the American School Health Association, Recommended Policies and Practice for School Nursing. J. School Health, *27*: 6-7, 1957.

Committee on Dental Health Programs in the Schools. A Report on the Role of the Dental Hygienist in Schools, J. School Health. *30*: 182, 1960.

Cromwell, Gertrude E.: School Nurse Is Part of the School Program. The Nation's Schools, *59*: 63-64, 1957.

Education Research Services, School Health and Nurse Services, Washington D.C., National Education Association, American Association of School Administrators and Research Division. Number 6. July, 1966. 40 pp.

Functions and Qualifications for School Nurses, American Nurses Association, Public Health Nurses Section. New York, The Association, 1960.

Joint Committee on Health Problems in Education of the National Education Association and the American Medical Association. *The Nurse in the School*. Washington D.C., National Education Association, 1955.

The Nurse in the School Health Program. J. School Health, *37* (Special Issue) 1967.

Related Backround Reading

Crow, Lester D. and Crow, Alice (Eds.): *Readings in Guidance*. 2nd Ed., New York, David McKay, 1962.

Elsbree, Willlard S., McNally, Harold J., and Wynn, Richard: *Elementary School Aministration and Supervision*. New York, American Book Co., 1967. (Chapter 18. Administering the Guidance Program).

Ferguson, Donald G.: *Pupil Personnel Services*, Washington, D.C., The Center for Applied Research in Education, 1963, pp. 46-47.

French, Will, Hull, J. Dan and Dodds, B.L.: *American High School Administration—Policy and Practice*. New York, Rinehart & Co., 1957. (pp. 315-320. The High School Health Service.)

Grieder, Calvin, Pierce, Truman M., and Rosenstengel, William E.: *Public School Administration*. 2nd Ed., New York, The Ronald Press, 1961. (pp. 203-206. Provisons for Guidance. pp. 307-313. School Health Program.)

Hand, Harold C.: *Principles of Public Secondary Education.* New York, Harcourt, Brace & Co., 1958. (Chap. 9. Providing for the Effective Guidance of Youth.)

Klausmeier, Herbert J. and Dresden, Katharine: *Teaching in the Elementary School,* 2nd Ed., New York, Harper & Bros., 1962. (pp. 572-73. Health Services.)

Matheson, Robert H.: *Guidance Policy and Practice,* 3rd Ed., New York, Harper & Row, 1962. (pp. 236-237. Health Services.)

Misner, Paul J., Schneider, Frederick W. and Keith, Lowell G.: *Elementary School Administration.* Columbus, Ohio, Charles E. Merrill Books Inc., 1963. (Chapter ll. Guidance: The "Coming" Area in the Elementary School).

Wilson, Robert E.: *Educational Administration.* Columbus, Ohio, Charles E. Merrill Books, Inc., 1966. (pp. 593-594. Student Counseling Services).

Zeran, Franklin R., and Riccio, Anthony C.: *Organization and Administration of Guidance Services,* Chicago, Rand McNally & Co., 1962. (pp. 205-208. Health Services).

Organizational References

American Dental Association, 222 East Superior Street, Chicago, Ill. 60611.

American Nurses Association, 2 Park Ave., New York, New York 10016.

National League for Nursing, 10 Columbus Circle, New York, N,Y. 10019.

U.S. Department of Health, Education and Welfare, Washington, D.C. 20025. (Children's Bureau, Office of Education, Public Health Service).

6

Information

Please

WHO'S WHO

HELEN YOUNG	*A 14-year-old-Girl in the Ninth Grade of the Chesterfield Junior High School*
PATRICIA NEWTON	*An English Teacher*
DANIEL SHORE	*Principal of Chesterfield Junior High School*
JESSIE HART	*School Nurse*
BILL DICKINSON	*Summer School Principal*
DR. JOHNSON	*School Physician*

When a teacher learns that the school administrator has deliberately withheld information about a student's history of epilepsy, she becomes incensed.

EVEN though there were no children in sight, one could tell from the atmosphere of the Chesterfield Junior High School that all was in readiness for them. The rooms had been scrubbed and freshly painted. The windows shone and the desks and chairs had new coats of varnish. There was activity, though not nearly as much as there would be on the next day when the students reappeared. Today only the teachers were on hand, arranging their desks, setting up records, checking books and materials — getting ready for the opening day of another school year.

Mrs. Newton, one of the English teachers, was busy at her desk when her Principal came into her room and said, "Pat, I've got another student for your home room — a new resident in the city — who just registered this morning. I've talked with her mother and thought I'd let you know about her before the onslaught tomorrow morning."

"I appreciate that, Mr. Shore," the teacher replied. "There is always some confusion on the first morning, and anything that will minimize it is helpful."

"Here is the usual information about her," Mr. Shore said as he showed a registration card to Mrs. Newton. "Her name is Helen Young. She lives over on Arden Street where her parents just bought a house. They used to live in Oakdale near the University where her father is a Professor of History. Maybe you've heard of him — Walter Young? I understand that he has written several books. At any rate, Helen had all of her previous schooling at the University Laboratory School. We don't have her complete record yet, but I expect to get it in the mail in the next day or two. I understand from her mother that she has not done particularly well academically and that she is at least a year behind in her reading ability. I'll fill you in on all of this as soon as I get the record. You'll want to know her reading scores because she is scheduled to be in your ninth-grade English section."

"O.K., Mr. Shore, I'll be on the lookout for Helen Young tomorrow. And I would appreciate your sending me the other 'vital statistics' about her when her records are transferred."

Helen Young did appear in Mrs. Newton's home room on the opening day of school. She was a slight, dark-haired girl who seemed a bit shy, a fact which Patricia Newton attributed to her unfamiliarity with the school and the other students. "This will all change," she thought to herself, "and I'll probably wish for this kind of quiet attention many times in the future. These kids change so fast from being scared newcomers to being one of the gang."

At the end of the week Mr. Shore told Mrs. Newton that Helen's records had arrived and he would like to go over them with her. As she entered his office, he greeted her and invited her to have a chair. "Here's what the Lab School record shows about the Young girl. Her age is 14, as we knew, and her reading level when she transferred was 7.3. Her I.Q. is shown here as 102. Height and weight normal. Vision and hearing O.K. The usual childhood diseases, but no indication of health problems. The only items of unusual interest

are two teachers' notations that Helen seemed nervous
and was a frequent behavior problem when she was
in kindergarten and first grade. One of them noted that
she threw an ink bottle."

"From my observation to date," Mrs. Newton responded, "she doesn't seem like a behavior problem at
all — in fact, just the opposite. She sits quietly at her
desk, does what she is asked to do, and seems to have
little interest in the other students. I have been expecting her to make friends with someone, or to show a
little enthusiasm about something, but so far, she has
been completely passive. According to these teachers'
comments, I guess things are bound to change, though
I hope not that drastically. Thanks for letting me know
about Helen."

"One more thing, Pat, I forgot to tell you. When
her mother was here she stressed the fact that they hope
Helen can be helped with her reading so that she can
catch up to grade level. As you might expect, her parents
are very interested in having her do well in school."

"I'll certainly do my best with the young lady," the
teacher replied as she left the office.

Mrs. Newton accepted Helen Young as a challenge.
The girl seemed to want to learn, but she was extremely
passive about the process. It was hard to get much
satisfaction from working with Helen, since there was
never that moment of happy discovery when pupil and
teacher alike rejoice in gaining some new understanding.
With Helen it was just plodding along, doing what she
was told, including staying after school on a few occasions so that Mrs. Newton could help her over some
humps that might have been obstacles in later classes if
she didn't grasp them then. The teacher pondered about
Helen. "There must be some reason for this girl's pas-
sivity. It just isn't normal for her to keep to herself all
the time, never socializing with the others. I wonder if
there could be anything on her health record that might
account for this?"

With this thought in mind, Mrs. Newton visited the school nurse one day shortly after the winter recess. "Mrs. Hart," she said, "I came to talk about Helen Young. She's in my home room and also in my English class — a new student this year. She is such a quiet girl, such a loner, that I'm concerned about her. I thought you might be able to shed some light on her behavior. Is there anything on her health record that might indicate a reason for it?"

"No, I'm sure there isn't," Mrs. Hart answered. "Of course, I'll check it for you if you want me to, but if there had been anything significant, I would have sent it to you early in the year with the list of your students' health problems that have special concern for you."

"I know there was nothing on that list, because I've checked it carefully. I've tried to guess at what might be her problem. Not vision or hearing, I'm quite sure."

"Well, let me look at the record, just to be certain." Mrs. Hart went to the locked filing cabinet where the records were kept, found Helen's and examined it, saying, "No, there's nothing indicated here. In fact, there is nothing on this card that I could say is out of the ordinary. It's probably just the girl's personality. Maybe her parents are domineering and her docility is her way of getting along with them. Anyway, I wouldn't worry about it. Most of the complaints I get are about students who are just the opposite. You ought to be glad you have a quiet one."

"Maybe so, but this one has me baffled. I'm glad to know that she has no special health problem, though." Mrs. Newton left the nurse's office, saying, "Thanks for the information, Mrs. Hart."

The rest of the school year progressed about as usual and everyone was glad when vacation approached, with its promise of summer weather and recreational activities.

Mrs. Newton had a feeling of satisfaction about the accomplishments of her students, particularly Helen Young with whom she had worked so diligently. Helen had upgraded her reading ability by one whole level, to 8.3. While not yet up to standard, it was a commendable improvement, and Pat Newton felt proud of it. She had a feeling that with a litle more effort she could help Helen improve even more, perhaps getting her score up to grade level before she moved on to the senior high school next year. With that thought in mind, she called Helen's mother late in the spring to suggest that she might want to consider summer school for Helen. "I'm going to be teaching a special class in remedial reading," she told the mother, "and I think Helen could profit by it, if you want to register her for it."

The mother was pleased at the suggestion and said that she would most certainly enroll Helen in Mrs. Newton's class. "We do appreciate all you have done for Helen, Mrs. Newton. Both Dr. Young and I have been so pleased to see the improvement in her grades this year."

Helen Young did seem to profit by summer school. Mrs. Newton could see the improvement as the last of the six-week session approached. Though still the same quiet, docile girl, Helen did volunteer occasionally to read out loud in class — something she had never done before.

It was in the last week of summer school, about ten minutes before the closing bell, when Helen Young finished reciting and instead of slipping quietly into her chair, suddenly started to jerk violently in convulsive movements. Her books flew and papers were scattered as she lost complete control of herself. The class was stunned, and so was Mrs. Newton momentarily. Realizing what was happening, she rushed to Helen to keep the girl from hitting furniture and other objects in her uncontrollable spasms and to make sure that she did not choke.

And then the whole thing was over almost as suddenly as it had begun. Helen looked a bit dazed, but insisted on getting into her chair, saying, "It's all right. I'm O.K."

Mrs. Newton told her to put her head on her desk and rest while she arranged to get the nurse who was in another building, but just then the dismissal bell rang. She excused the other boys and girls from the room.

"I'm all right, Mrs. Newton," the girl kept saying.

"I'm sure you are, Helen, but I would like to send for the nurse. She's in the District Office and it will take her only five minutes to get here to be sure you are all right."

"Oh, please don't call the nurse, Mrs. Newton. My mother wouldn't like it. She would be very angry with me, and she's probably waiting outside in the car for me now. I'm all right. Please let me go."

"All right, Helen, but I want to walk out with you. I think I would like to talk with your mother."

"Please, Mrs. Newton, I'm all right. My mother wouldn't like it if she knew I made a scene. There's nothing wrong."

In spite of the girl's protestations, the teacher accompanied her to the front of the school building, where her mother was indeed waiting for her. She had a neighbor and her child in the car too, and Helen climbed into the back seat quickly and quietly.

"Mrs. Young," Mrs. Newton began, not knowing what to say, especially in the presence of strangers, "I think Helen might not be feeling well. I'm sure she'll tell you what happened, but I think she needs some rest when she gets home."

"I'm all right, Mother," Helen protested from the back seat. "I just dropped my books in class and everybody got scared."

"Oh, I'm sure she's all right, Mrs. Newton. She sometimes has little spells. Thanks for your interest, but it's really nothing." With that the mother drove off.

Mrs. Newton was stunned with disbelief. Most of the mothers she knew would become concerned immediately. In fact, many tended to overprotect their children. Here was a mother who didn't even want to hear about an incident that was serious enough to cause a teacher to accompany the child out of the building. This seemed like a strange reaction.

As she walked back into the building, Mrs. Newton became more convinced than ever that she was right in thinking that Helen had some health problem. Could she be an epileptic? Certainly the girl had endured a seizure, even though it was of short duration. But why was there no record of a problem of this degree of severity?

She went directly to the principal's office and told him what had happened, and ended up by saying, "I have a suspicion that this girl is an epileptic. But why is there no record of it?"

Mr. Dickinson, a teacher from one of the other schools in the city who was serving as summer school principal, said, "I don't know anything about this girl. But since she's a regular student here during the school year, I suggest that you call Dan Shore. He's spending his vacation at home during this summer, and I'm sure he wouldn't mind."

"I'll do that, Mr. Dickinson, but I know he doesn't know anything about her either, since I've already discussed Helen Young with him on several occasions."

Nevertheless, Mrs. Newton did call Mr. Shore at home. When he came to the telephone, she said, "Mr. Shore, I think I know now what's wrong with Helen Young. She had a seizure in my class today."

"So now you know," the Principal replied matter of factly.

"Did you know she is epileptic?" the teacher almost shouted in disbelief.

"Yes, I've known it from the beginning, but I must tell you that I was sworn to secrecy by her parents. They didn't want anyone to know about it. They told me that she is on medication which prevents seizures, and that there is no reason whatsoever for teachers to know about her condition. The fact that she did have a seizure today makes me think she isn't getting the right dosage."

"Did Mrs. Hart know about this too?"

"Yes, the parents did permit me to tell our school nurse, just in case there might be an emergency of some kind. But I told Mrs. Hart that she must not tell anyone."

"So she knew too. It isn't fair not to tell teachers about a condition like this. You know it isn't. And I want you to know that I don't like it at all."

"Now calm down, Pat. I asked Dr. Johnson whether or not it was all right to keep this information confidential in this way, and he agreed. But tell me, what would you have done differently if you had known about Helen?"

"Perhaps nothing, but at least I could understand why the girl is so docile. And maybe I wouldn't have pushed her so hard to upgrade her reading."

"You see," Mr. Shore responded, "that's just the point. Her parents think that's the reason she is behind in reading ability. You see, her teachers at the Lab School did know about the epilepsy, and they handled Helen with kid gloves. They didn't demand much from her, and she didn't have to do everything she would have if this condition were not known to them. Now, you didn't know about it, and you worked with the girl as you would with any other child and actually brought about a phenomenal improvement. Isn't that true?"

"Yes, I guess so. But I should have been told about the possibility of an emergency so I'd know what to expect."

"You know what to do in case of a seizure — all teachers do. And you apparently did just the right thing when it did happen. As a matter of fact, there is little that one can do. And the likelihood of it happening is so remote — you can't believe that it is worthwhile to put yourself on guard all the time for something that will probably never happen. The drugs that are available these days are remarkable in controlling the situation."

"O.K., Mr. Shore, I guess the thing that bothers me most is that I'm not considered professional enough to be able to keep information confidential. I resent being treated as though I might spread information like this around to people who shouldn't know about it."

"Look, Pat, if I had told you, I would have had to tell every other teacher that Helen has epilepsy. That's at least five people. Nothing is confidential when that many people know about it. And for what purpose? I can understand the position of the parents. I would feel just the same way if Helen were my child, wouldn't you?"

DISCUSSION QUESTIONS

1. How much information about a student should be included on records transferred to a new school?

2. How confidential should health information be kept? Are there certain types of health information that should not be shared with classroom teachers? If so, what?

3. Do you think that certain kinds of knowledge about a child might influence a teacher's expectations of that child?

4. If Helen Young had been injured during the seizure she sustained in class, could the school have been held liable for negligence?

5. What do you think was the effect of Helen Young's seizure on the other students? If Mrs. Newton had known of Helen Young's condition, do you think she should have prepared the rest of the class for the possibility of a seizure?

6. What effect would the knowledge of Helen's condition have on the educational and vocational guidance by school counselors?

7. If the Youngs move to another community, what health information should be sent to the new school?

8. If Mrs. Newton had known that Helen Young was an epileptic, do you think she would have treated her any differently?

Selected References

The School Health Issue: The Confidentiality of Health Records.

American Academy of Pediatrics: Report of the Committee on School Health. Evanston, Illinois, The Academy, 1966. (Chapter 2. Health Records and their Confidentiality.)

American Medical Association: Report of the Fifth National Conference on Physicians and Schools, Chicago, The Association. (p. 13-17. Use of Health Records. p. 48. The Confidential Nature of Medical Information.)

Bruyn, Henry B.: Confidentiality in the Use of Health Records, J. School Health, *37*: 161-165, 1967.

Joint Committee on Health Problems in Education of the National Education Association and the American Medical Association: *Health Appraisal of School Children*, 2nd Ed., 1961. (p. 6 and 7. Nature and Scope of Health Records.)

Joint Committee on Health Problems in Education of the National Education Association and the American Medical Association: *School Health Services*, Washington, D.C., The Associations, 1964.

National Committee on School Health Policies: *Suggested School Health Policies*, 4th Ed., Washington, D.C., 1966. National Education Association and the American Medical Association.

The Epileptic Child in School

Byrd, Oliver E.: *School Health Administration*, Philadelphia, W.B. Saunders Co., 1964. (p. 483-484. Description of the Detroit and the Denver Program for Epileptic School Children).

Earle, Howard: What Are We Doing About Epilepsy? Today's Health, *44*: 28-31, 84, 88, 1966.

Harlin, Vivian K.: Experiences with Epileptic Children in a Public School Program, J. School Health, *35*: 20-24, 1965.

Lampe, John M.: Education and Epilepsy, J. School Health, *29*: 220-223, 1959.

Linde, Shirley M.: What Most People Don't Know About Epilepsy, Today's Health, *42*: 38-41, 53, 54, 1964.

Nemir, Alma: *The School Health Program*, Philadelphia, W.B. Saunders Co., 1959. (pp. 206-214. Epilepsy).

Tenny, John W., and Lennox, Margaret A.: Children with Epilepsy, J. School Health, *23*: 39-40, 1952.

Related Background Reading

Cromwell, Gertrude E.: School Nurse is Part of School Program, The Nation's Schools, *59*: 63-64, 1957.

Elsbree, Willard S., McNally, Harold J., and Wynn, Richard: *Elementary School Administration and Supervision*, 3rd Ed., New York, American Book Co., 1967. (pp. 217-219. Physically Atypical.)

French, Will, Hull, J. Dan and Dodds, B.L.: *American High School Administration — Policy and Practice*, Rev. Ed., New York, Rinehart & Co., 1957. (pp. 315-320. The High School Health Service.)

Grieder, Calvin, Pierce, Truman M. and Rosenstengel, William E.: *Public School Administration*, 2nd Ed., New York, The Ronald Press, 1961. (Chapter 14. Special Education Program.)

Hand, Harold C.: *Principles of Public Secondary Education*, New York, Harcourt, Brace & Co., 1958. (p. 211. Discovering Educationally Significant Facts About Students.)

Klausmeier, Herbert J. and Dresden, Katharine: *Teaching in the Elementary School*, 2nd Ed., New York, Harper & Bros., 1962. (p. 537. Orthopedic Handicaps and Chronic Illnesses.)

Mackie, Romaine P.: Special Education Reaches Nearly 2 Million Children, School Life, *47*: 8, 1964.

Mackie, Romaine P., *et al.*: What You Should Know About Teaching Handicapped Children, School Management, *11*: #10 91-112, #11, #12, 1967.

Misner, Paul J., Schneider, Frederick W., and Keith, Lowell G.: *Elementary School Administration*, Columbus, Ohio, Charles E. Merrill Books, Inc., 1963. (Chapter 10. Pupils with Problems: The Maladjusted & Handicapped. pp. 304-307. Health Services.)

Nemir, Alma: *The School Health Program*, Philadelphia, W.B. Saunders Co., 1965. (pp. 240-241. Physican, School Nurse. pp. 282-284. The Cumulative Health Record. Appendix B. School Health Records & Forms.)

Voelker, Paul H., *et al*: *The Education of Exceptional Children*, Rev. Educational Res., *33*: 5-138, 1963.

Waleski, Dorothy: The Physically Handicapped in the Regular Classroom, NEA J., *53*: 13-16, 1964.

Wilson, Rebert E.: *Educational Administration*, Columbus, Ohio, Charles E. Merrill Books, Inc., 1966. (pp. 564-569. Special Education. pp. 609-610. The Nurse.)

Organizational References

American Medical Association, 535 North Dearborn St., Chicago, Ill. 60610.

Council for Exceptional Children, 1201 16th St., N.W., Washington, D.C. 20036.

Epilepsy Association of America, 111 W. 57th St, N. Y., N. Y. 10019 U. S. Department of Health, Education and Welfare, Washington, D.C. 20025. (Children's Bureau, Office of Education, Public Health Service.)

Healthful School Living

7

What's Cooking

The relatively small percentage of students who buy a complete lunch in the secondary school cafeterias prompts a Board of Education to ponder the wisdom of curtailing the school lunch program in order to reduce the school budget.

THE clock showed 8:05 P.M. as Mr. Edwin Hughes, President of the Fulton Board of Education, tapped his pencil on the table and said, "I think we should get started. We're already five minutes late, and we'll be lucky if we get out of here by midnight."

The other four Board members stopped their conversation and gave their full attention to the President, who said, "I appreciate your getting here on time tonight because we have a lot of work to do. It's the 10th of January and we must begin the process of putting the school budget together. We might as well start by asking Al to give us the financial picture as he sees it. I believe he has some preliminary figures for us."

Alfred Lee, Business Manager of the School District, cleared his throat and started, "It should be no surprise to you that we're facing a substantial increase in our budget for the next school year. We all recognize that school costs are going up. The only question is, how much. These estimates will show that by merely maintaining our current program without any fundamental changes, we can anticipate a substantial jump in the tax rate. In addition, Dr. Scott indicates that we can also expect to have a slight increase in the total number of pupils, and that we will need at least four new teachers. This may not be the kind of budget you are eager to present to the community, but the fixed costs you will see on these sheets don't seem to leave much choice."

Mr. Lee handed out the material he had prepared and the Board members began their review of the figures. After a few minutes, William O'Connell, the newest member of the Board, spoke up. "This is my first experience in making up a school budget. I realize that there are certain built-in expenses which simply cannot be trimmed. But there *must* be some items which could be eliminated, postponed or at least reduced without hurting our educational program for next year."

"We have tried to think of every possibility of reducing our requests," replied Dr. Kenneth Scott, Superintendent of Schools, "and for the past two years we have postponed some of the building repairs that were not absolutely essential. But now I'm afraid that these projects, which you will see in the maintainence category, simply cannot be put off any longer. That's the reason they are included in these preliminary figures along with other items which are absolute musts. Also, we'll have to maintain a salary schedule that puts us in a favorable position to compete for the best teachers. It's probably no consolation to you, but most of middle-class suburbia is faced with this same problem."

"I guess we all realize that," Mrs. Dorothy Hansen, the only woman Board member said. "And if we have to ask for more money again this year, we'll just have to do it. I wouldn't want to see our program curtailed, and I don't think the community would either."

"I agree," said Harry Sherman, Vice-president of the Board, "but I do think it's important for us to study the situation thoroughly to be sure there's no place we can cut down. If we establish that, we'll be in a stronger position in May when we explain to the voters that we have done everything in our power to reduce or eliminate those parts of the budget which are not absolutely essential. I would hate to see anything happen to the curriulum *per se*, but I am wondering if we might not take a good hard look at some of our services."

"Well, we'll never know unless we start," said Robert Owen, the remaining Board member. "Let's review these figures from first to last so that we can make some reasonable judgments."

For the next three hours, Dr. Scott and Alfred Lee explained the preliminary budget step by step, indicating the projected costs for next year and explaining the basis upon which they had arrived at the proposed figures. A few items that did not seem to be absolutely essential were either postponed or trimmed, but the Board refused to tamper with class size or existing educational programs.

During the discussion the Board members reflected the strong community pride in its schools. Many residents had made the move to Fulton because they wanted their children, most of whom were preparing for college, to get a good education. At the same time, Board members were also mindful of the fact that there had been an increase in the school budget every year since World War II, and many of their constituents were beginning to complain about the constantly rising taxes. In order to obtain approval for the budget, the Board needed to be able to assure the community that it was getting full value for the tax dollars. The voters had never let them down before, but the Board was cognizant of an increasing number of "no's" each year. Last year the budget barely eked through, and the turnout was large.

At 11 o'clock, when every item had been discussed, Mr. Hughes sat back and said resignedly, "Well, it looks like at least a 10% increase over last year, and we haven't even begun to negotiate with the teachers."

"Let me tell you about that situation," said Dr. Scott. "The staff expects and, if I may say so, deserves a substantial increase. If this is granted to the teachers, it will mean proportionate raises for the non-professional staff as well. And, of course, this means an increase in social security, retirement and fringe benefits. Frankly, lady and gentlemen, I think our preliminary budget figures are conservative, and we might as well face the music and think in terms of an overall 15% increase for next year."

There was a moment of silence, and then Mr. Hughes said, "It's getting late and I think we've done enough for one evening. If it's agreeable with all of you, I think we ought to mull over these figures for our homework and meet again next week to talk further about them."

The shuffling of chairs indicated general approval with this suggestion and the meeting was adjourned.

When the Board convened again the following week for another round in the battle of the budget, Robert Owen started the discussion by stating, "I've been doing a lot of thinking about our finances this past week. I studied the budget figures carefully, mentally challenging every expenditure to see if there isn't some place we can save money, and I've found one service that is hard for me to justify here in Fulton. I'd like to hear your ideas about it. I'm referring to the school lunch program in our junior and senior high schools. We are fortunate in not needing to serve lunches in the elementary schools since the distance factor is so small that most of the kids can go home at noon. But the secondary schools' lunch program costs us a lot of money. I checked with Al Lee and Dr. Scott during the week and they sent me some figures provided by Mrs. Knight, the Director of our school lunch program. These statistics give a pretty good picture, not only of the cost, but also the number of students who buy their lunches at school. Al, would you be good enough to distribute this information to the other Board members?"

As the business manager handed some mimeographed material to each of the Board members, Dr. Scott interjected, "While you're digesting these figures, and there is no pun intended, I think it would be in order for me to review the background of our school lunch program.

"We have always served food in our junior and senior high schools simply because our students live too far away to go home for lunch. Back in the early days, practically all of the boys and girls brought their own lunches from home. Then during the 30's we began to get donations of food from the federal government in order to help it get rid of some surplus commodities. As a matter of fact, the schools, through the lunch program, really helped to stabilize the farm economy. Many of these surplus commodities are still available today and provide a substantial part of the noon meal we serve. Perhaps some of you are old enough to remember that during those depression days the school lunch was the main meal for many kids. During the 40's the national school lunch program was expanded, and we began to get financial help from the federal government if certain types of lunches were made available to the students. One of the stipulations of this program was, and still is, that the lunch include one hot dish, a vegetable and milk. This is referred to as the Type A luncheon. Today we serve such a lunch at the two junior high schools and at the senior high. We sell it for 40¢ and we are reimbursed 9¢ from the federal government for each such meal sold.

"As Mr. Owen pointed out, we never did find it necessary to serve lunch to our elementary school pupils. Fortunately, they live close enough to school to get home for lunch, but I'll have more to say on that later.

Where there is an undue family hardship such as a working mother, children are permitted to bring their lunches to school. However, the two junior high schools and the high school are so located that it is impossible for the large majority of students to get home for lunch during the 40-minute period allotted to it."

Mrs. Hansen broke in with a question. "Not everyone buys this hot lunch, though, do they?"

"Oh, no. However, I must point out that in addition to the Type A lunch, there is a variety of sandwiches available, as well as the usual ice cream, potato chips, etcetera. Some students choose this, and of course, there is no federal subsidy for the sale of these items."

Bob Owen then said, "Let's get to the question of the number of students who eat in the school cafeterias."

Dr. Scott continued, "In our junior high schools all students must stay in the building unless they receive their parents' written permission to go home. They have a full period for lunch — that's 40 minutes and, as you can see from the statistics, about 25% of the junior high students buy the Type A meals and an additional 50% buy on the a la carte plan. The rest bring their own lunches.

"In the senior high, the picture is quite different. The students are not required to remain in the building, but may leave. They too have a full 40-minute lunch period. Mrs. Knight tells me that approximately 5% of our high shool students order the Type A lunch, and approximately 20% buy sandwiches, milk, et cetera on the a la carte plan. When all the costs of running the cafeterias are totaled up, it costs the School District about $20,000 plus, annually, to subsidize the school lunch program — and this doesn't include cost of equipment, maintenance and other hidden costs such as the use of faculty time for supervision."

"Do you mean to say that only about 25% of all of the senior high school students eat lunch in the cafeteria?" Mr. Sherman asked.

"Yes, that's the story, although you can always count on a few more on rainy days," Dr. Scott answered. "I'm sure you all understand the problems we face. The high school is located near a shopping center, and there are three or four 'greasy spoons', an ice cream shop, a couple of delicatessens and a bakery within five minutes walking time. Our students patronize all of them. The Principal and Mrs. Knight have tried numerous ways to encourage the high school students to buy their lunches in school, but we haven't had much luck. The surroundings in the cafeteria are pleasant; there is ample room, and the food, although not gourmet, is good. The menus are planned to include favorite teen-age foods—in fact, the very ones they buy elsewhere at noon. But the sad fact of the matter is that the students want to get out of the school building, and eating in one or another of these places in the shopping center has become a social symbol. You are simply not a part of the 'in' group if you eat your lunch on school premises. Also, from our observations, it is perfectly apparent that many of our high school students want to go out for a smoke or to be with a current 'steady'.

"As for the junior high school kids, they have no choice. They have to eat on the school grounds. But, as the figures show, only 25% of them eat the hot meal. With them, it seems to be considered by many to be 'square' to eat the school food, especially the hot plate. That's why so many bring their own sandwiches, supplementing them with milk or ice cream. We've tried every possible way of promoting our school lunch program in the secondary schools. We send advance monthly menus to the parents, we've talked to the PTA's, and we have tried to get the teachers to emphasize the good qualities of our lunch program. But I'm afraid the situation is not going to change much from what it is now."

Dorothy Hansen then said, "My 16 year old told me about Mrs. Knight's talk to the G.O. regarding the need for well-balanced lunches, but Jean said that the kids were not impressed. She said, 'After all, Mother, we have to watch our weight and even though Mrs. Knight promised to offer spaghetti, hamburgers, frankfurters and pizza often, we don't see why we have to have vegetables with them. I think the meal we get at night will take care of what we might miss at noon. Besides, we like to get out for a while before the afternoon classes start.' I've offered to make sandwiches for her, but she would rather have the 40¢ and be with the rest of the kids. To be perfectly candid with you, I did the same thing when I was in high school, and I don't believe I am any the worse for it."

"The sad part of this," said Mr. O'Connell, "is that we offer every possible inducement for the students to buy a good lunch for a reasonable price. I wish I could buy such a meal for 40¢. I can remember when we built our high school and renovated the two junior high schools. We gave a lot of attention to providing a nice environment for eating and making sure that there were adequate convenient washing facilities. We hired an excellent Director and the administration scheduled sufficient time for eating a decent meal. Yet, the cafeterias are not being fully used. When I talk with the junior high school boy who lives next door to me, he tells me that he would rather bring a sandwich and a bag of potato chips and buy milk, since coke is not available, than buy a Type A meal or even a sandwich at school. He claims the sandwiches aren't always the kind he likes, and he'd rather use his allowance for snacks after school. That bakery does a whopping business. If you don't believe me, drop in around 3:30 any day after school and you'll find that you have to stand in line."

"The fact remains, though," interjected Dr. Scott,

"that about one-fourth of our junior high school students do buy the Type A meal and an additional 50% buy at least a sandwich lunch every day. Practically everyone buys something to drink, usually milk. In the high school the situation is not as good, but we do service about a fourth of the student body."

"There are three things that really bother me," William O'Connell said. "One is that we are trying to operate a lunch program as if we were back in the '30's and 40's under the the illusion that we are helping the agricultural situation in the country, and at the same time, furnishing a wholesome meal for children who might not otherwise get one.

"The second is that we are scrounging around for every penny we can get in order to furnish quality education to a community that demands it, but at the same time is screaming because of the increase in taxes necessary to provide that education.

"If these two factors weren't enough to make me question the need for our current lunch program, then the third one alone is enough to make me really unhappy. We make the claim that this noonday meal is both educational and healthful. In view of the statistics we've seen, I am not so sure that it is either. To be blunt, I would rather see us put the $20,000 we use to subsidize the lunch program into teachers' salaries and new educational programs than to continue this service under the present conditions."

"There is one additional fact that must be considered," Robert Owen stated. "I'm referring to the length of time set aside for the lunch period. Frankly, I question the need for having a full 40 minutes. With the increased emphasis on academic preparation for so many of our college-bound students, it seems almost wasteful to let students utilize all this time to roam around and eat nothing but a hamburger and a coke."

At this point Edwin Hughes said, "From what I

hear, you doubt the need for our current lunch program, particularly in the High School, and this may be a valid question. It's an important consideration and I don't believe it would be wise for us to take any formal action on this matter this evening. There are many things to take into account before we can resolve it. As I see the questions they are: (1) Should the Type A lunches be eliminated from our secondary schools? (2) Should the Type A lunch be eliminated only from the high school? (3) Should the amount of time allotted for the lunch period be cut down — with or without the Type A lunch? If so, how much? (4) Should we eliminate the entire lunch program and substitute some vending machines which will provide milk, sandwiches, ice cream and fruit?"

Dr. Scott then said, "I hope the Board will give this some serious thought before making any decision. We might be considering action that would prove to be penny wise and pound foolish. I've checked with other school districts in the area, and the cost of subsidizing their school lunch programs range from 7 to 15% of their total cost. Ours happens to be 15%.

"I think you should also recognize another factor before you consider cutting down on our lunch services. Many of the mothers of our elementary school students are beginning to put pressure on the administration to permit their children to stay in school for lunch whether the mothers are home or not. They claim they're sick and tired of acting as chauffeurs and insist that since some students are permitted to stay at school for lunch anyhow, all should be allowed to do so. Some mothers have even volunteered to supervise! I hope the Board will take all of these factors into account when our current school lunch policies are being reviewed."

DISCUSSION QUESTIONS

1. What are the various alternatives for solving the school lunch problem in the Fulton School District?

2. What should be the criteria for the Board's decision concerning the school lunch program?

3. Is there justification for the secondary school lunch program as a positive educational experience?

4. How much time should be allotted for the lunch period?

5. Should Fulton High School students be permitted to leave the school grounds during the lunch period?

6. How do you think the students would feel about a possible curtailment of the school lunch program?

7. Should the feelings of the teachers about this matter be sought and considered?

8. If vending machines were utilized in lieu of the current system, how would this affect the need for lunchroom personnel?

9. How do you think the parents in the Fulton School District would feel about a change in the secondary school lunch program?

10. Would your thinking about this case be altered if the Fulton School were not located near so many eating places?

11. Comment on the growing number of requests by elementary school mothers to allow all students to stay in school for lunch?

12. If all elementary school students were permitted to stay, should the Fulton School District provide a hot Type A lunch?

Selected References

The School Health Issue: The Need for School Lunch Programs.

Agricultural Marketing Service, U.S. Department of Agriculture: The National School Lunch Program, Fifteen Years of Progress, PA No. 469, 1961. The Superintendent of Documents, U.S. Printing Office, Washington, D.C.

Anderson, C.L.: *School Health Practice*, 3rd Ed., St. Louis, The C.V. Mosby Co., 1964. (Food Service, pp. 449-453)

Bryan, M. de G.: *School Cafeteria*, 2nd Ed., New York, Appleton-Century-Crofts, 1958.

Cronan, Marion L.: *The School Lunch*, Peoria, Ill., Charles A. Bennett Co., 1962.

Elsbree, Willard S., McNally, Harold J., and Wynn, Richard: *Elementary School Administration and Supervision*, 3rd Ed., New York, American Book Co., 1967. (Food Sevices, pp. 476-479)

Grieder, Calvin, Pierce, Truman M. and Rosenstengel, William E.: *Public School Administration*, New York, The Ronald Press, 1961, (School Lunch Program, pp. 302-307)

Haag, Jessie Helen: *School Health Program*, New York, Henry Holt & Co., 1958. (School Nutrition, pp. 173-214)

Joint Committee on Health Problems in Education of the National Education Association and the American Medical Association: *Health Aspects of the School Lunch Program*, 2nd Ed., 1962. 30 pp. Single copy 35 ¢ from the American Medical Association, 535 North Dearborn Street, Chicago, Illinois, 60610.

Misner, Paul J., Schneider, Frederick W. and Keith, Lowell G.: *Elementary School Administration*, Columbus, Ohio, Charles E. Merrill Books, Inc., 1963. (Food Services. pp. 301-304)

National Committee on School Health Policies: *Suggested School Health Policies*, 3rd Ed., 1962. Published and distributed by the Joint Committee on Health Problems in Education of the National Education Association and the American Medical Association, Chicago, Illinois. (School Food Service, pp. 8-10)

Nemir, Alma: *The School Health Program*, Philadelphia, W.B. Saunders Co., 1959. (School Lunch Program, Confections and Carbonated Beverages in Schools, pp. 44-46.)

Smolensky, Jack and Bonvechio, L. Richard: *Principles of School Health*, Boston, D.C. Heath & Co., 1966. (School Lunch Programs, pp. 96-98 and Food Seevice, pp. 272-275; 285-286.)

U.S. Office of Education, *The School Lunch — Its Educational Contribution*, Washington D.C., U.S. Government Printing Office, 1957, 27 pp.

Wilson, Charles C., (Ed.): *School Health Services*, Joint Committee on Health Problems of the National Education Association and the American Medical Association, 2nd Ed., 1964.(School Lunch Program, pp. 349-350.)

Wilson, Robert E. (Ed.): *Educational Aministration*, Columbus, Ohio, Charles E. Merrill Books, Inc., 1966. (Food Services in Schools pp. 235, 250, 276, 676-7, 712-21.)

Wilson, Robert E.: Eleven Headaches and Four Tranquilizers, The Nation's Schools, 60: 66-72, 1957.

Organizational References

U.S. Department of Health, Education and Welfare, Washington, D.C. 20025. (Children's Bureau, Office of Education, Public Health Service.)

8

I Know, Butt...

A high school faculty faces the problem of whether or not to modify the school smoking prohibition for Juniors and Seniors

DR. Edward Farnsworth, Principal of the Rockwood High School, adjusted the microphone and greeted his faculty. "Ladies and gentlemen, I hope all of you have had an opportunity to have some coffee. Now, if you would be kind enough to take seats, we can get our meeting started."

The teachers slowly took chairs in the high school cafeteria, obviously reluctant to break off their informal conversations. When all were seated, the Principal, peering over his glasses, began the session.

"I don't intend to keep you very long this afternoon. I realize that you have many things to do like getting final exams ready and preparing your year-end reports. As you know, our only agenda item is the smoking question, and since we have spent a good deal of time during the year discussing its pros and cons, this meeting should serve as a wrap-up of what we might call Rockwood's 'burning issue'.

"Before we proceed with making a decision, I'd like to review our problem and briefly summarize the salient points of our previous discussions.

"Last October the Student Council presented us with a petition seeking permission for student smoking during lunch periods and for an hour after school dismissal in the afternoon. The smoking privilege, if approved, would be limited to the Commons area of our new high school to be opened next fall, and would be extended only to 'those junior and senior students who submit written parental permission'. The petition states that Council members will help the custodians in the daily clean-up of the smoking area.

"The student appeal is based on their claim that smoking is going to take place in school anyhow. Our own experience with the surreptitious smoking in the lavatories, locker rooms and other out-of-the-way places would seem to bear out this contention.

"In our formal and informal discussions of this issue during the year, we have expressed substantial arguments on both sides. Now we must make a decision. The Superintendent has indicated that the Board will undoubtedly accept our recommendation as the policy they adopt for the District. As far as safety is concerned, I have checked with the Fire Department and established the fact that the Commons area in the new high school is considered a safe area for smoking and will be so designated. Smoking will be permitted there after school hours by those attending plays, concerts and meetings held in our building. As for the high school students, there is a state law which prohibits them from smoking on school grounds, but this law has long been openly violated by a number of school districts. In fact there is a serious question about the law's constitionality, and it may even be challenged in the courts. At any rate, the decision has been thrown into our laps.

"Before we take a vote, let's review the pros and cons of this issue. Without question the most important reason for denying the Student Council petition is that cigarette smoking is a health hazard. We have been made aware of this by the Surgeon General's reports on Smoking and Health, the latest of them released in 1967. If we permit students to smoke on school property, it might seem that we are ignoring the warning, and that we are in essence actually encouraging students to smoke."

"Right," thought one of the high school health teachers. "When I think of all the hours I spend trying to get across to our kids the dangers of smoking, it makes my blood boil to have these facts contradicted by the deliberate sanctioning, and perhaps actual encouragement of smoking. What's the use of showing all these films from the Cancer Society and the Heart and T.B. Associations, if we then say, 'now you're not in class, go ahead smoke if you want to'. I try to influence these kids not to smoke, and then we turn around and say 'it's really O.K. if you want to'. If this petition is approved, you can be sure that when I'm on lunch duty, I won't allow the kids from the health classes to smoke. After all, I don't care how much students learn about the statistical relationship between smoking and lung cancer, but I do care whether they take up the habit of smoking cigarettes, especially under school auspices."

"I disagree," thought the Art teacher, "If we're going to have rules against smoking, we shouldn't use that health hazard argument. If smoking were really as dangerous as some of those fear-mongers would have you believe, the government would stop the television advertising, and maybe even take cigarettes off the market. There are plenty of doctors who smoke, and if anyone should be aware of danger, they should. I don't hear the American Medical Association trying to convince people not to smoke. Of course, there may be other reasons for not letting kids smoke in school, but the danger to health certainly is not convincing enough at this stage of the game. We would do much better if we concentrated our attention on the air pollution problem which really is a health hazard, rather than wasting our time prohibiting something the students are going to do anyway. Let's be sure that smoking *is* harmful before we go on this crusade."

"On the other hand," the Principal continued, "we want our students to learn how to think critically and to make decisions for themselves. Whether or not to smoke is just one of those decisions, and while we hope to influence it, we can't mandate it. Smoking is an accepted practice. Many of us smoke and so do some of the parents, and we know that some of our students will decide to smoke in spite of the medical evidence. If we maintain that they should be making their own decisions, then we ought to let them make them."

"Right," thought the Social Studies teacher. "This is exactly what we try to do our Social Studies classes. We take care to consider all sides of issues, whether we agree with them or not, and the students have to come to their own decisions. We shouldn't make smoking appear as a prohibition determined and enforced by adults. We would do better to present it as a young adult's choice. I'm getting sick and tired of teaching the importance of personal decision making in a democracy, and then imposing restrictions that don't allow this process to take place. It negates everything I'm trying to do. If these kids are old enough to be drafted soon after they leave school — if they're old enough to drive cars, then they are old enough to decide about smoking."

"I disagree," thought the Industrial Arts teacher. "These kids aren't really old enough to make an important decision like this that could affect their whole lives. I think there is too much permissiveness today, both at home and in school. That's one of the reasons we have so much trouble with kids — we've given them too much of a voice and too many rights, and they simply haven't had enough experience to be able to make responsible judgments. I don't know what schools are coming to. Just imagine — teenagers questioning the rules of the school! What they need to learn is how to be a part of a democracy by following the rules that exist. We're getting too lax in every way — the way we permit them to dress for school is scandalous."

The Principal cleared his throat and then continued. "One of the most persistent arguments for prohibiting smoking by the students is that the younger students tend to copy the older ones in their anxiety to gain sophistication. I don't have to tell you that there's a lot of difference between 15-year-old sophomores and 17 or 18-year-old seniors. The older ones who get permission for smoking will set the pattern for the younger ones who will want to follow suit. I can just hear them telling their parents in plaintive tones, 'the other kids smoke, why can't we?'"

"Right", the Guidance Counselor thought to herself. "The research that revealed the positive correlation between student smoking habits and low scholastic achievement could be duplicated right here. Many of our students who are having academic difficulty are the ones who belong to the smoking crowd that congregates just past the limits of the school grounds. If we allow smoking on school premises, it's like saying to these smokers, 'it's O.K.' And the younger students may get the idea that smoking is the adult thing to do. With the increasing competition for college entrance, we should discourage anything that might detract students from their concentration on their studies."

"I disagree," thought the Biology teacher. "By the time they get to high school these kids have been exposed to smoking and most of them have at least experimented with it. Many of them have already determined their own pattern. Whether we allow smoking here or not won't make a bit of difference. It's what happens in the fifth and sixth grades and the junior high schools that could have some influence on them. Like so many of the things we do, it's too little or too late, and high school is much too late to deal with these emotion-fraught topics like smoking, especially by an unenforceable regulation. We don't need to fool ourselves: if their parents smoke, the kids are almost sure to do the same, in spite of any 'educational program' we carry on at school."

"Then we hear the argument," the Principal said, "that today's boys and girls are maturing physically at an earlier age. Certainly they are much more sophisticated in their knowledge of current problems in spite of their foolish antics. What's more, they are genuinely concerned about their own part in improving society. You hear them talk about awareness of what is going on. The whole world is a 'happening' to them and they want to be in it. In my 30 years in education, I've never seen kids with more real concern about social issues than the ones who are in high school right now."

"Right," thought the English teacher. "I am constantly amazed at the depth of understanding that these kids display, especially about current social problems. In my ten years as faculty advisor for the student newspaper, I've seen a marked change especially in the topics that students write about. They are terribly interested in civil rights, in war and peace and even in politics. Our school paper used to be filled with complaints about the lack of school spirit, the food in the cafeteria and gossip about who was going with whom. But, today that sort of thing is de-emphasized. Students are showing their ability to analyze problems, to discuss them openly and their confidence in taking a position. Students like these will approach the smoking issue in the same way, I'm sure, and their decisions will be at least as good as the adults' decisions. Let's not be the authority figures, telling them what they should do. If we decide on a no-smoking regulation, we're probably making smoking more attractive simply by prohibiting it."

"I disagree," the Dean of Boys thought to himself. "I've seen a lot of students in my day, and kids are still kids. They only try to act older. Maybe it's because they've got more money, some even have cars and most of them start dating a lot earlier. But that isn't because they are more mature. They're just pushed into it by their parents. Why, by the time they're 16, they've experienced just about every thrill there is. But they are still just kids underneath — pretending to be adults. They still want some firm direction. In fact, they're begging for it. I know, I talk with boys every day about difficulties of one sort or another, and most of them wouldn't be having problems if they had some firm direction from the adults."

"Then," the Principal went on, "we can't overlook the fact that many of our students, whose parents permit them to smoke, are actually under age to purchase cigarettes legally in the State. If we let them smoke in

school, then aren't we in effect, showing our disagree-
ment with the law and also encouraging students to
disobey it?"

"Right," thought the Dean of Girls. "I'm glad that the
issue of legality has finally been stated. If it's against the
law for young people to purchase cigarettes, then the intent
of the law is clear. They are not supposed to smoke. How
in the world can we run the school unless we enforce the
rules which our government has made for good reason. It
only encourages young people to disregard law and order
if we teachers disregard it. And such disdain for law can
extend to other more important restrictions too. So many
of the girls who are brought to my office for discipline
are also the ones who smoke at an age when it is illegal
for them to purchase cigarettes. And when they are
brought in for violating the school smoking restrictions,
their general attitude is that they were foolish to get caught.
They see nothing wrong in violating the rules. The school
just can't afford to be in a position of flaunting the law by
saying to kids 'you're not old enough to buy cigarettes,
but if you can get them one way or another, you can
smoke them here'."

"I disagree," the Commercial teacher thought to himself.
"Rules and laws that cannot be enforced should be re-
examined and even challenged, and this smoking prohibition is surely one of those laws. It's practically impossible
to supervise vending machines to be sure no minors buy
cigarettes from them, so the law literally has no effect.
Besides, if parents give their kids permission to smoke, they
will not hesitate to buy cigarettes for them. I don't think
the school decision should be made on the basis of an
unenforceable regulation."

"Of course, there is another angle on this that may
seem to be of minor importance," the Principal said,
"but several of you raised this problem. If we retain
our no-smoking rule, we have the nuisance to trying
to enforce it. We all know what that is like, especially
those of you who do hall and school grounds duty.
It's almost impossible to control the smoking that goes

on in the girls' and boys' lavatories. Kids get caught time after time and are not fazed in the least by disciplinary measures. As a matter of fact, their disdain for authority seems to add an aura of glamour that brings admiration from their peers for their callousness to the rules and reprimands. It's just as difficult to enforce the no-smoking rule during the lunch hours when students are permitted to leave the building. We know that they simply move out to the edge of the school ground limits and smoke there where no one can stop them."

"Right," thought the Mathematics teacher, President of the Teachers' Association. "Teachers shouldn't have to be policemen for seeing that rules are enforced. We've been fighting long enough to get rid of these non-professional duties. Allowing the kids some smoking privileges might relieve the situation. For teachers to have to patrol the halls and grounds is a waste of time and money, and actually sets up the wrong image of a teacher. I certainly don't need a master's degree in mathematics in order to patrol the lavatories and school grounds. If it has to be done, the school board should hire some parents to do it — that would save money. I don't think the parents would be any more effective than we've been, but they ought to see what the situation is. They might gain some appreciation of our problem when we negotiate with the School Board to get rid of such non-teaching duties."

"I disagree," thought the Physics teacher. "If everyone would pitch in and do his share, it really wouldn't be the problem Dr. Farnsworth suggests. The trouble now is that some teachers think they shouldn't do anything except teach their own subject, and that's all. Heaven knows I don't like these onerous duties, but when I have to police an area, the kids don't get away with anything! I think we ought to accept our responsibility and do it right. Kids respect teachers who enforce rules. They may not realize it at the time, but they surely appreciate it after they leave. Many of my students come back and tell me so."

"Then there are the parents and their viewpoints,"

Dr. Farnsworth continued. "You remember the January meeting of the PTA and the student panel discussion entitled 'To Smoke or Not To Smoke?' They presented the pros and cons for allowing students to smoke during the lunch hour or after school, many of them the same points of view expressed in our several faculty discussions. Then, you will recall, an opinion poll was taken. The results were interesting but not helpful to us. Among the 212 parents who attended, there was almost even distribution between the pros and cons."

"I'm not sure how I would mark such a questionnaire," the French teacher said, as she extinguished her cigarette. "There are times when I wish someone had had more influence on me during high school so that I might not have started to smoke. On the other hand, I wouldn't like to have anyone tell me that I couldn't smoke in school at all. I think I know how the students feel. After all, I'm only five or six years older than some of them. It wasn't so long ago that I was sneaking smokes in the girls' room too. I was lucky enough not to get caught. If we decide to keep the no-smoking restriction, I wonder if the next step won't be the forbidding of smoking in the teachers' room too? I wish I knew the right way to vote. The no-smoking rule doesn't seem to work. Maybe legalizing smoking would take away its glamour so that it wouldn't have the appeal of forbidden fruit. I just don't know what would be the best thing to do."

"I'm not sure how I would mark such a questionnaire," the Basketball Coach thought to himself. "Of course, I wish none of our kids smoked at all, and I'll always do all I can to discourage the practice. I tell my teams that it just doesn't do them any good, and they know I feel strongly about it and that I don't smoke myself. Yet, after the season is over, I've seen some of the varsity boys smoking off the school grounds, and in a few instances, on the school grounds. I think they respect the smoking prohibition during the season, but only because I enforce it with the threat of their being dropped from the squad. I don't need to kid myself into thinking that I am influencing their smoking practices for life. And these kids aren't hoods either — they're really the cream of the crop. Maybe it would be better for them to smoke in the open. I don't know what would be the best thing to do."

"I believe I've summarized all of the pertinent arguments for and against the student petition," the Principal concluded. "And now it's up to us to make a decision. The secretary will now hand out the ballots on which you should check yes or no to indicate your approval or disapproval of the petition. As you leave, drop your ballots in the box by the door, and I'll let you know the results tomorrow."

DISCUSSION QUESTIONS

1. What do you think of the philosophy behind the students' claim that "smoking is going to take place anyhow"?

2. Under what circumstances should a school administration consider violating a law? Can you cite any instances in which schools have done this?

3. How much voice should student councils have in determining and implementing school policy?

4. Comment on the statement that "smoking will be permitted in the commons area after school hours by those attending plays, concerts and meetings".

5. Comment on the points of view held by each of the teachers. Which one do *you* believe should carry the most weight in reaching the decision for Rockwood High?

6. Is it reasonable to expect a faculty to make this decision? If not, how and by whom do you think the student smoking regulation should be made?

7. Do you think teachers should be permitted to smoke on school property?

8. Do you think a teacher who smokes can be effective in teaching young people about the hazards of smoking?

9. How would you vote, if you were member of the faculty?

Selected References

The School Health Issue: *Student Smoking in Schools.*

American Ass'n for Health, Physical Education and Recreation: *Smoking: The School's Responsibility*, Washington, D.C., The Association, 1964.

Brandes, L.G.: Policies with Regard to Smoking, National Association of Secondary School Principals Bulletin, *45*: 1961.

Brecher, Ruth, *et al.*: *The Consumers Union*; *Report on Smoking and the Public Interest*, Mt. Vernon, New York, Consumers Union, 1963.

Byrd, Oliver: *School Health Administration*, Philadelphia, W.B. Saunders Co., 1964. (Tobacco Education, pp. 117-120.)

Horn, D.: Cigarette Smoking in the High Schools, California School Health, II, No. 1: 17-21, 1966.

Horne, Tom: Smoking and Health — The Activities of a High School Student Committee, J. School Health, *33*: 451-456, 1963.

Keeve, J. Philip: Smoking Habits and Attitudes of 3057 Public School Students and their Families (Newburgh, N.Y.), *35*: 458-459, 1965.

Lawton, M.P.: Psychology of Adolesent Anti-Smoking Education, J. School Health, *33*: 337-345, 1963.

Radelfinger, Sam (Ed.): Cigarette Smoking, A special issue of California School Health, II, No. 1: 34-31, 1966.

Rogers, K.D. and Reese G.: Smoking and High School Performance, Amer. J. Dis. Child., *108*: 117-121, 1964.

Salber, E. J., *et al.*: Reasons for Smoking, Given by Secondary School Children, J. Health and Human Behavior, Summer, *4*: 118-129, 1963.

Salber, E.J. and MacMahon, B.: Smoking Habits of High School Students Related to Intelligence and Achievement, Pediatrics, *24*: 780-787, 1962.

Salber, E.J. and MacMahon, B.: Cigarette Smoking among High School Students Related to Social Class and Parental Smoking Habits, Amer. J. Publ. Health, *51*: 1780-1789, 1961.

Sallak, V.J.: A Study of Smoking Practices of Selected Groups of

Junior and Senior High School Students in Public Schools in Erie Co., N.Y., J. Schools Health, *31*:, 307, 1961.

Schwartz, Jerome L. and Dubitzky, Mildred: Research in Student Smoking Habits and Smoking Control, J. School Health, *37*: 177-182, 1967.

Smoking and Health, Report of the Advisory Committee to the Surgeon General of the Public Health Service, Public Health Service Publication No. 1103, U.S. Government Printing Office, Washington, D.C., 20021, 1964, 450 pp.

Weaver J.D.: How to Stop Student Smoking, School Management, March, 1964.

Related Background Reading

Bronfenbrenner, Urie: The Split-Level American Family, Saturday Review, L, # 40: 60-66, 1967.

Burton, William H.: *The Guidance of Learning Activities*, New York, Appleton-Centry-Crofts, 1952. (Chapter 10. The Teacher is a Member of a Group of Learners.)

Cantor, Nathaniel: *The Teaching-Learning Process*, New York, Dryden Press, 1953. (Chapter 4. The Classroom Atmosphere.)

Cummings, Oneta: *The Effective Student Council*, The National Association of Secondary School Principals, Washington, D.C., 1964.

French, Will, Hull, J. Dan and Dodds, B.L.: *American High School Administration — Policy and Practice*, New York, Rinehart & Co., 1957. (The Student Council, pp. 251-254.)

Kirkendall, Lester A. and Zeraw, Franklin R.: *Student Councils in Action,* New York, Chartwell House, 1953. (Chapter 11.)

Miel, Alice, et al.: *Cooperative Procedures in Learning*, New York, Bureau of Publications, Teachers College, Columbia University, 1952. (Chapter VIII, pp. 197-231.)

National Association of Student Councils: *The Student Council in the Secondary School*: Washington, D.C., National Association of Secondary School Principals, 1962.

Watenberg, William W. (Ed.): *Social Deviancy Among Youth*, Chicago, National Society for the Study of Education, 65th Yearbook, Part 1, 1966.

Wellington, C. Burleigh and Wellington, Jean: *Teaching for Critical Thinking*, New York, McGraw-Hill Book Co., 1960.

Organizational References

American Association for Health Physical Education and Recreation, 1201 Sixteenth St. N.W., Washington, D.C. 20006

American Cancer Society, 219 East 42nd Street, New York, New York 10017.

American Heart Association, 44 East 23rd Street, New York, N.Y.10010.

American Medical Association, 535 North Dearborn Street, Chicago, Illinois 60610.

National Congress of Parents and Teachers, 700 North Rush St., Chicago, Illinois, 60011.

National Tuberculosis Association, 1740 Broadway, New York, N.Y. 10019.

U.S. Department of Health, Education and Welfare, Washington, D.C. 20025 (Children's Bureau, Office of Education, Public Health Service).

Health Aspects of
Physical Education

9

Smotherhood

Despite medical advice that her child's heart murmur is innocent, a mother insists that her son be excused from physical activity in school.

"I believe you're next, Mrs. Concord. I'm sorry I kept you waiting, but these few days before school are very busy for us school nurses. Won't you and your son sit right here by my desk, and as soon as I get your health record filled out, you can go to the kindergarten and meet Miss Farley. Would you like to tell me your name, young man?"

"Ralph," the boy replied shyly, looking down at his shoes and clutching his mother's hand for dear life.

"Well, that's fine, Ralph. My name is Mrs. Darrow, and any time you're not feeling well at school, I'm the one who'll take good care of you." The nurse then turned to the mother. "Now let me see, Mrs. Concord. There are a number of questions we'd like answered so that we know more about your son's physical condition. This will help us in planning his school program as well as to be prepared for any emergencies that might arise. Also I would be glad to answer any questions you might have about our school health services."

"I appreciate this very much, Mrs. Darrow," the mother replied. "I'm very concerned about Ralph's health, and I want to be sure the school takes good care of my boy. He's an only child, you know, and he's very precious to me and his father."

"I'm sure he is," the nurse replied. "But why don't

146

we get on with the information that's needed for his school health record. May I see Ralph's birth certif-cate?"

The next few moments were taken up with Mrs. Concord furnishing answers to the routine questions on the school medical form. The first questions dealt with shots, childhood diseases and vaccinations.

"Has Ralph ever had any other diseases?" the nurse asked. "Asthma, epilepsy, T.B?..."

"None of those," the mother replied, "but he does have a heart condition."

"I see," Mrs. Darrow said, glancing over at Ralph, who, during this time, sat docilely by his mother. "Say, wouldn't it be a good idea if we sent Ralph out to the school playground? Some of our sixth-grade boys and girls have volunteered their services to supervise the new kindergarteners, and one of them could take Ralph out and watch him while he plays."

"No, thank you," the mother said. "Ralph under-stands his limitations and there is nothing to hide."

"O.K.," the nurse replied with a sigh. "Tell me about Ralph's 'heart condition'."

"I'll be glad to. Ever since Ralph was born, I was afraid that something might be wrong with his heart. You see, my father had a heart attack when I was still in high school. The doctor told him he would be O.K., and, after three months of convalescence he returned to his office and he seemed to get along fine. Then he had another heart attack, and this time he died. I myself had rheumatic fever as a child, and I've always had to be careful about overexerting. After my father died, I realized how important it is, in spite of what doctors say. My doctor says I am all right, but I just don't trust him. Then, when Ralph came, I worried about him. He was a healthy, normal boy until two years ago. I took him to the pediatrician for a check-up, and that's when I found out that Ralph has a heart murmur. The doctor assured me that it was an innocent murmur, and that there was no need to limit Ralph's activities, but I just don't want to take any chances. That's why I want to make sure that the kindergarten teacher understands that my Ralph must not play in any active games. I'm sure you can understand my feeling, Mrs. Darrow."

The nurse was silent for a moment, and said, "I'm trying to, Mrs. Concord. But before I make any comments, what is your pediatrician's name?"

"Dr. Gerard Lake. He's right here in town."

"Is he the person we should contact in case of an emergency that might occur when you or Mr. Concord are not available?"

"Of course, Mrs. Darrow. But let me assure you I will always be available during the mornings when Ralph is in school. And, of course, I'll be taking him to and from school every day. I'll do my shopping in the afternoons; I don't mind taking Ralph with me."

Virginia Darrow sighed and said, "If he can't play with the other children, Ralph will be missing a lot of fun, and since your doctor has given him a clean bill of health..."

"Just a moment," Mrs. Concord interrupted. "Do you call a heart murmur a 'clean bill of health'?"

"I do, if a competent physician has diagnosed it as being 'innocent'."

"Well, I don't, Mrs. Darrow, and I don't want Ralph to be exposed to any unnecessary risks."

"I'm not asking you to do that, Mrs. Concord, but there's nothing to be gained by pursuing this any further. Our school physician, Dr. Charles Griffin, will be here in about three weeks to begin giving health appraisals to those children who haven't had one during the past year. If it's agreeable with you, I'd like to ask him to check Ralph immediately."

"By all means," the mother replied. "I'd be happy

to have another medical opinion. I don't mind telling you that Dr. Lake is the third doctor I've taken Ralph to and they all say the same thing. Maybe Dr. Griffin will make a better diagnosis. Please have him call me as soon as he's seen Ralph. Meanwhile, I want to insist that my son's activities be strictly limited. That's not asking too much. After all, he's only in kindergarten and I'm sure there are no gym classes involved."

"No, he won't be in 'gym', but kindergarteners can be quite active, you know, Mrs. Concord. I'll have a chat with Miss Farley later today and tell her what you have said about limiting Ralph's activities. Meanwhile, you take him to the kindergarten to meet his teacher, and get acquainted. I'll let you know Dr. Griffin's recommendations as soon as he's had a chance to examine Ralph."

After Mrs. Concord left with Ralph in tow, the nurse thought to herself, "I suppose I should be thankful in a way that the child is so subdued. It's a relief from the way kids usually climb the walls during this interview. But I do feel sorry for poor Ralph. I doubt whether he'll ever die of a heart attack. He's more apt to 'smother' to death first."

After she had interviewed the last of the kindergarten applicants, Mrs. Darrow walked to the kindergarten and found Ann Farley straightening up the room.

"Still in one piece, Ann?"

"I'm a little weary, Virginia, but frankly I'm glad to get back. Now that I've had a year's experience, I feel like a real veteran. Looks like I have a pretty good group, too, if I'm any judge."

"I agree, Ann, and you can take that from a hard-bitten veteran of six years. They seem to be a pretty healthy lot, too, except for...."

"I know," the kindergarten teacher said. "Except for Ralphie-boy. The way his mother talks, I have a

severe cardiac case on my hands. Just how serious is
this murmur?"

"I don't think it's serious at all," the nurse answered.
"But I don't think we should take any chances until I
get the word from Dr. Griffin. Let me tell you what
Mrs. Concord told me."

As the nurse told of her interview with the mother,
it became quite apparent that substantially the same
story had been related to Ann Farley. The teacher
added, "That kid just sat there as meek as a lamb
throughout the whole story. This was going on, mind
you, while other mothers and children were arriving
and I'd have to break off our conversation to greet
them. But Mrs. Concord just sat and waited for me to
get back to her after each interruption and she'd pick
up her tale of anxiety just where she left off. And not
a peep out of Ralph. I did notice, though, that he
seemed anxious to be with the other kids."

"That doesn't surprise me, Ann. He seems to be
an intelligent child. But I suggest you keep him busy
without too much exertion for the next two or three
weeks, and maybe we'll get some help from Dr. Griffin."

"I'll try," the teacher replied wearily. "But it won't
be easy to give him much special attention when there
are 28 other five-year-olds to look after. And if I have
to deal with Mrs. Concord when she delivers Ralph
each morning, I'll consider that above and beyond the
call of duty. But don't worry about him, Virginia. I'll
see that Ralph will be O.K."

During the third week of September, Dr. Griffin
came to school to set up the schedule for health examinations with Virginia Darrow. "There's one child
I'd like you to check as soon as you can," the nurse
told Dr. Griffin. She then gave the doctor a summary
of her interview with Mrs. Concord. "And," she concluded, "Ralph is now in the morning kindergarten
class seemingly getting along very well. Miss Farley

tells me Ralph is quiet, plays well with the other children while they're in class; but when it's time to go out on the playground he sticks close to the teacher and will do nothing except go on the swings or see-saws. He won't play any active games. Miss Farley isn't sure, but she thinks she's seen Mrs. Concord watching from the other side of the school fence on several occasions when the class was outside for play. In any event, the mother is always present at dismissal, and she wastes no time in picking up the child. The way she protects him is really quite pathetic."

"Did you say that Gerard Lake is their pediatrician? He's one of the finest in the business. What I don't understand is why he didn't send us a note indicating his diagnosis and his recommendations."

"If she had any information from Dr. Lake, Mrs. Concord did not show it to me," the nurse replied. "She did have records of all Ralph's immunizations, but that's all."

"O.K., Virginia, I think we'll work it this way. I'll be here on Thursday; that's the day after tomorrow. Let's start with Miss Farley's class. Let her know so that she can use tomorrow to prepare those kids who need examinations. This would include Ralph. I know you and the teachers have some routine about alerting the chidren so that they won't think they're being led into lion's den. I'll check Ralph and make my own diagnosis. Then I'll give Lake a ring and compare notes. I hope you can keep Mrs. Concord off my back until I have something definite to tell her. I'm sure when the kids go home tomorrow and the parents go through the routine of 'What did you do today?' Mrs. Concord will get more out of Ralph than 'nothing'!"

"I think you're right, Dr. Griffin," Virginia Darrow replied with a smile, "Mrs. Concord has already called me three times and asked when you would be examining Ralph. I've been purposedly evasive each time. So I can't guarantee a thing. See you Thursday."

When Dr. Griffin arrived at school on Thursday, a well-planned routine had already been set in motion. Those classes with pupils who were to be examined were alerted by Virginia Darrow. The teachers discussed with candor the forthcoming examinations at the various grade levels. The helpfulness and ease of the examination was stressed and everyone was assured that no shots were to be given. Reliable older pupils were used to take a few children out of each class at one time to the nurse's office and then helped maintain order while one child at a time went in. The first children examined were always chosen by the teacher for their leadership qualities in the class. Thus, when they left after the examination which took about five minutes, they made it quite clear to those waiting outside the nurse's office and to those still in the classroom that all was well. Remarks such as, "Gee, it didn't hurt at all," or "He's a nice guy," or "I think I want to be a doctor when I grow up" were not uncommon.

Miss Farley's group was the first to be examined, and when Ralph came into the office, he had the same shy look that Virginia Darrow noticed when she had first seen him. The boy smiled when he was introduced to Dr. Griffin and submitted to the examination without a word. The doctor checked the boy's throat, skin and hair while making complimentary remarks about the boy's looks. When it came time to check the boy's heart and lungs, Ralph volunteered, "I know what that is. It's a stethoscope. I've seen it a lot. It tells you about my bad heart. My mother told me."

"Well, let's see about that," the doctor said as he adjusted the instrument to his ears. For the next two or three minutes the physician listened intently to the boy's heart beat, shifting the instrument from one spot to the other. When he was through, he asked Ralph to slip on his shirt and said, "Son, you sound O.K. to me. I tried hard, but can't hear anything that would stop you from playing just like the rest of your friends."

"That's what the other doctors said," Ralph replied. "But Mommy says I have to be very careful. Maybe someday I can play beseball when I'm older if I don't run too much now."

When the boy left, the doctor turned to Virginia and said, "That's about the most innocent murmur I've heard in a long time. That kid shouldn't be restricted in any way. Do we have anyone waiting now?"

"There are two more left from this group."

"Well, let me see them and then see if you can reach Dr. Lake. I'd like to talk with him. Hold up the next group for a few minutes until I see whether I'll be able to talk with him."

Ten minutes later Dr. Griffin did talk with Dr. Lake. The school physician identified himself and then said, "I don't want to take up too much of your time, but I am interested in getting a report on one of your patients, Ralph Concord. I just got through examining him and I'd appreciate getting your evaluation of this boy's heart."

For the next few minutes, Dr. Griffin listened intently and made a few notes from time to time. He then said, "Well, that pretty much jibes with what we think here. The murmur is clearly associated with pulmonic ejection. The boy should not have to be restricted in activity. How about writing another note and sending it on to me? I'll see what I can do here. Many thanks for the information. I'll keep in touch with you and let you know what happens."

After he hung up, Dr. Griffin turned to Virginia Darrow and said, "Dr. Lake completely confirms what we've surmised. That kid's murmur is as innocent as they come. Lake has examined him three times in the last year and he sees no reason why Ralph should be restricted in any way. Furthermore, at least one other pediatrician has seen the child and comes up with the same report. But that mother is the stumbling block. The last time Lake saw her he told her again that the child needs no restrictions. He thought he had made some headway with her, but I told him he hadn't. He is going to send me a note with his diagnosis and a statement that no restrictions are necessary. We can put that in Ralph's health record. Now, let's see what we can do about Mrs. Concord. I'm sure she will be parked outside the office after she comes to pick up Ralph, and we might as well settle this today. Please alert Miss Farley to come in too."

Shortly after the morning kindergarten session had been dismissed, Mrs. Concord, with Ralph in tow, did indeed ask to see Dr. Griffin. Miss Farley also came to the nurse's office. The doctor insisted, however, that Ralph not stay with his mother during the discussion. The boy was seated outside the office with a coloring book, and, as usual, obeyed, and quickly became absorbed in his task.

"Did you examine my boy this morning?" Mrs. Concord asked.

"I did," the doctor replied. "I found that he has a murmur which I would report as being innocent. I was able to call Dr. Lake after I had made the examination, and, without telling him my findings, asked him for information about Ralph. He told me that he has examined your boy on several occasions, and is familiar with the murmur and is certain about its innocence. This was the same conclusion I had reached independently. Both he and I concur that no restriction in physical activity is indicated. You have a healthy, normal boy, Mrs. Concord, and I think he should be permitted to participate fully in the school program along with his classmates."

"How can you say he's healthy when you just told me that his heart is not normal? Are there any other children in his class that have these murmurs?"

"Of course, there are, Mrs. Concord. I picked up two more this morning, and I'll refer them to their own family physicians for a recheck. And that's about par for the course. National statistics indicate that these innocent murmurs of various types occur about 30 per cent of the time in children."

"I'm not interested in statistics, Dr. Griffin. They quoted them to me about my father too, but after he went back to work, he died. When I hear you and Dr. Lake say that there is something wrong with the functioning of my boy's heart, I'm not willing to take any chances."

"Wait a minute, Mrs. Concord. I did not say that there is something wrong with the functioning of Ralph's heart. The sound of his heart is normal for him. This isn't a matter of taking chances."

There was a moment of silence and Ann Farley stated, "All of us are interested in Ralph's well-being. The doctors say there is no danger of your boy being hurt by permitting him to indulge in normal play. Since this is so, I can see a great deal of harm coming to Ralph if this type of restriction is imposed. He will develop unnecessary fears. His relationships with his peers will be negatively affected, and it seems a shame to allow this to happen to this bright and alert boy."

"Yes," the mother retorted, "all of us may be interested in my child's well-being, but if anything happens to him, I'm the one who really suffers. If he's laid up because of a heart attack, then the only relationships he'll have with his peers is when they come to visit him. No, thank you."

"As it happens," Virginia Darrow said to the mother, "Ralph is only in kindergarten this year and all games and play activities will be supervised by his teacher, Miss Farley. The same will be true with the other classroom teachers he will have up until the time he takes physical education taught by a specialist in the fourth grade. When that time comes, no one is excused from gym without a medical request. That's a state law, you know. What will you do then if his condition remains the same as now?"

"I'll cross *that* bridge when I get to it," Mrs. Concord replied. "But as long as you brought it up, I think we're rapidly getting to the point in this country where the individual doesn't count any more. The way flouridation is imposed on the public certainly illustrates that. But to get back to Ralph's situation, if Miss Farley lets my boy participate in those strenuous games with the other children, then I'm taking him out of school. There's no law that says Ralph must go to kindergarten, anyhow. I'll send him to some private nursery school if I can afford it. And if I can't, I'll just keep him at home. At least I'll know he'll be safe there. I'll bring him back to school only when I have to, and we'll see about this gym business! Now, if you'll excuse me, I'll leave."

Mrs. Concord stopped outside the door just long enough to take Ralph by the hand, and they headed for the school exit. As they left, she was heard to say, "Come on, you poor child. I'll fix you a nice hot lunch when we get home and then you can take your nap."

When the mother left, the three staff members looked at each other for a moment. With a sigh, Dr. Griffin got out of his chair, picked up his medical bag and walked to the office door. He turned and said, "Good luck, girls."

DISCUSSION QUESTIONS

1. Was Mrs. Concord justified in her demand that Ralph's activities be restricted? If so, why?

2. Comment on the value of school health appraisals.

3. Discuss the way that school health appraisals were handled in this case.

4. If you were Ralph Concord's classroom teacher, what would you do in a conflict situation of this type?

5. Can Ralph be forced to take physical education?

6. Do you think that most private physicians would take the same position that Dr. Lake did?

7. Where there is a difference of opinion between a school physician and a private physician about a child's physical condition, who has the final authority in determining whether a child's school program should be modified?

8. What would you suggest as the best approach to solving the problem of requests for excuses from physical education?

9. What do you think Mrs. Concord will do now?

10. What would you do if you were the school nurse?

11. Could this situation have been prevented? If so, how?

Selected References

The School Health Issue: Excuse from Physical Activity.

American Association for Health, Physical Education and Recreation: *Answers to Health Questions in Physical Education*, Washington, D.C., The Association, 1959.

American Medical Association, Committee on Exercise and Physical Fitness: Need for Varied Activities in Physical Education Programs, Johper, *36*: 6, 8, 1965.

Bureau of Educational Research, New York City Board of Education: Adolescents with Cardiac Limitations, J. School Health, *32*: 364, 1962.

Classification of Students for Physical Education, J.A.M.A. *199*: 265-267, 1967.

Hamburg, Morris: Educator's View of the Cardiac Child, J. School Health, *28*: 41-48, 1958.

Hamburg, Morris: Medical and Physical Activity Forms for the Cardiac School Child, New York St. J. Med., *64*: 1333-1335, 1964.

Hein, Fred V.: Health Classification vs. Medical Excuses from Physical Education, J. School Health, *32*: 14-17, 1962.

Miller, R.A., Smith, J., Stamler, J., *et al.*: The Detection of Heart Disease in Children, Circulation, *25*:85-95, 1962.

Murdock, C. George: Excuse from Physical Education, J. School Health, *37*: 387-389, 1967.

Nemir, Alma: *The School Health Program*, Philadelphia, W.B. Saunders Co., 1959. (Chapter 12. Heart Problems of Children and Youth.)

Report of the Seventh National Conference on Physicians and Schools, American Medical Association, Bureau of Health Education, Chicago, Ill., 1959. (pp. 83-102. Classification of Pupils for Physical Education.)

Whitehouse, Frederick A.: 'Cardiacs' Without Heart Disease: The World's Most Useful Neurosis, J. Rehabilitation, *33*:14, 1967.

Health Service Personnel and Medical Examinations

Bonvechio, L.R. and Dukelow, D.A.: Responsibilities of School Physicians, J. School Health, *31*: 21-30, 1961.

Cromwell, Gertrude E.: School Nurse is Part of School Program. The Nation's Schools, *59*: 63-64, 1957.

Cushman, George L.: Responsibility of the Family Physician, J. School Health, *31*: 340-344, 1961.

Dukelow, Donald A. and Hein, Fred V. (Eds.): *Health Appraisal of School Children*, 3rd Ed., Washington, D.C., National Education Association, 1961.

Joint Committee on Health Problems in Education of the NEA and AMA, *Health Appraisal of School Children*, Chicago, the American Medical Association, 1961. 56 pp.

National Committee of School Nurses of the American School Health Association: Recommended Policies and Practices for School Nursing, J. School Health, *29*: 1959.

Nemir, Alma: *The School Health Program*, Philadelphia, W.B. Saunders Co., 1959. (Appendix B. School Health Records and Forms. pp. 350-371, pp. 240-241. Physician, School Nurse.)

Wallace, Helen M: Utilization of Private Physicians and Dentists in School Health, J. School Health, *34*: 65-68, 1964.

Wilson, Robert E.: *Educational Administration*, Columbus, Ohio, Charles E. Merrill Books, Inc., 1966. (pp. 609-610. The Nurse.)

Related Background Reading

Elsbree, Willard S., McNally, Harold J. and Wynn, Richard: *Elementary School Administration and Supervision*, 3rd Ed., New York, American Book Co., 1967. (pp. 217-219. Physically Atypical.)

Hand, Harold C.: *Principles of Public Secondary Education*, New York, Harcourt, Brace Co., 1958. (p. 211. Discovering Educationally Significant Facts About Students.)

Klausmeier, Herbert J. and Dresden, Katharine: *Teaching in the Elementary School*, 2nd Ed., New York, Harper & Bros., 1962.(p. 537. Orthopedic Handicaps and Chronic Illnesses.)

Langton, Clair V., Allen, Ross L., and Wexler, Philip: *School Health — Organization and Services*, New York, The Ronald Press, 1961.

Mackie, Romaine P., *et al.*: What You Should Know About Teaching Handicapped Children, School Management, *11*: #10, 1967, #11, 1967, #12, 1967.

Misner, Paul J., Schneider, Frederick W., and Keith, Lowell G.: *Elementary School Administration*, Columbus, Ohio, Charles E. Merrill Books, Inc., 1963. (Chapter 10. Pupils with Problems: The Maladjusted and Handicapped. pp. 304-307. Health Services.)

Quillan, Warren W.: The Family Doctor and School Child Health, J. School Health, *31*: 121-124, 1961.

Voelkner, Paul H., *et al.*: The Education of Exceptional Children, Rev. Educational Res., *33*: 5-138, 1963.

Waleski, Dorothy: The Physically Handicapped in the Regular Classroom, NEA J., *53*: 13-16, 1964.

Organizational References

American Association for Health, Physical Education and Recreation, 1201 16th St., N.W., Washington, D.C. 20006.

American Heart Association, 44 E. 23rd St., New York, N.Y. 10010.

American Medical Association, 535 North Dearborn St., Chicago, Ill. 60610.

American Nurses Association, 2 Park Ave., New York, N.Y. 10016.

U.S. Department of Health, Education and Welfare, Washington, D.C. 20025. (Childrens' Bureau, Office of Education, Public Health Service.)

A Health Program for the Handicapped

10

Stop The World, I Want To Get On

WHO'S WHO

DR. LOWELL	*Principal*
MRS. MERRIAM	*Secretary*
LAURA MANN	*Third-grade Student*
MRS. MANN	*Laura's Mother*
DR. JOSEPH GROSS	*School Psychologist*
DR. GRANT	*Psychologist*
SALLY NORTON	*Third-grade Teacher*
MARIAN HILL	*Third-grade Student*

An emotionally disturbed child transfers from a special private school to Miss Norton's third grade in the Pittsville public school district and poses new problems for all concerned.

"Dr. Lowell, I hate to interrupt you, but Mrs. Mann is here to see you. She has an appointment for three o'clock, but she's early. Can you see her now?"

Dr. Lowell looked up from the mass of papers on his desk and said, "You might as well send her in. It'll be a welcome relief from these directives that our beloved Superintendent dreams up every year before school opens. Most of them will wind up in file 13 anyhow. And, oh yes, Mrs. Merriam, thanks for the coke. Not every principal has such a thoughtful secretary as I do. I don't know how school would keep without you."

"Forget it. The truth is that I wanted a coke myself — it's so warm this afternoon. And I felt sorry for you having to come in during the last week of August. Too bad Labor Day had to fall so early this year."

When Mrs. Mann came into Dr. Lowell's office and took the proferred seat, the Principal saw a well-dressed middle-aged woman who seemed somewhat nervous as she started to speak.

"I've been looking forward to this visit, Dr. Lowell, and I just didn't know how to kill time, so I thought I'd come over now. Do you mind if I smoke?"

"It's quite all right, Mrs. Mann. Here, have one of

mine. I can't break the habit myself. Maybe we'll have better luck with the kids. Now, what can I do for you?"

"I'm here to talk to you about my daughter, Laura. She was nine last spring. But let me tell you a little about the rest of our family first. We have two older boys, one will be a sophomore at the State University and the other will be a senior at East High School. We expect he'll be going on to college too. Incidentally, both of them attended this school, but that was before your time. You've been here about four years, I believe."

"That's right. I was delighted to have the chance to come to Lincoln. I've always considered it one of the best in the Pittsville District."

"We do too. We've lived in Pittsville for 15 years now, and we like it here. My husband has a retail business in the center of town and we've lived in this neighborhood ever since we moved here. We like the Pittsville schools, and particularly this one. That is why I'm here today.

"I never registered Laura for kindergarten at Lincoln because she has had a psychological problem. We suspected there was something wrong when she was just a baby, and by the time she was three there was enough evidence available both from our own observations and the pediatrician's to warrant our taking her to a psychiatrist. I won't bother you with the details, but when she was five, he recommended that she be enrolled in the kind of school where she could get individual attention.

"We've been sending her to the Morrow School for the past four years, a small private school suggested by the psychologist Laura is seeing now. It does very well with emotionally disturbed children. It's located just outside the city limits.

"I hate to tell you what this has been costing us, but that's beside the point. The reason I'm here is that there's been a definite improvement in Laura's behavior—so much so, that our psychologist thinks that she would benefit by being in a normal school environment with children her own age. All the neighborhood kids know her and play with her after school as well as on weekends and vacations. I've hesitated to come to you about letting Laura come to Lincoln, but I understand that your third grade classes are going to be quite small this year, so here I am. Maybe this will give her the chance she's never had. What are the possibilities of accepting her?"

Dr. Lowell had listened in silence as Mrs. Mann's story unfolded. The distressed mother was close to tears when she stopped talking, so the Principal waited a moment before he spoke.

"Let me begin by saying how much I admire the way you and Mr. Mann have handled this matter. I can appreciate the trials and tribulations you have been going through and the courage it has taken to face up to the realities of the situation.

"Now let's look at some of those realities so far as the school is concerned. Laura is eligible to attend the Lincoln School. After all, you live in this District. But, if her actions are so atypical that she is a disruptive influence in the class, then it is my right to exclude her. Now please don't misunderstand me. I am not implying that we do not have disruptive children in the school. We sure do, and there are days when the teachers and I are almost convinced that the disruptive ones outnumber the others. But this is an occupational hazard that we accept.

"However, there *are* some children who, for one reason or another, are so disruptive in the classroom that the teacher cannot cope with them. In those instances, we have to seek help. Of course, the parents are involved, and, depending upon the individual case, the school nurse, the attendance officer and the school psychologist may also be called upon. But, sometimes, no matter how hard we try, we can't seem to get at the root of the trouble, and it becomes necessary for me to exclude a child from attendance at school. That is done only when the involved professional personnel make such a recommendation, and it, too, is subject to review. In the instance of disruptive behavior, our psychologist's recommendation must be verified by a psychiatrist.

"That's a little background about school policies regarding enrollment. Now, Mrs. Mann, let me comment on those third grade statistics. It is true that our third grades are quite small. In fact, they'll average out to about 24 for each of the four sections. I don't know why they're so small—I've always kidded the PTA about my lack of control over birth rates, birth dates and moves in and out of the District. Anyhow, that's the way it is for this fall.

"But what is just as important as a small class, especially for Laura, is that here at Lincoln, we are trying to break out of the lock-step known as homogeneous grouping. At least, we're giving it a try, and since these third-grade classes are small, we think we'll do as well with the children by mixing them up rather than grouping them by some standard at this stage of their development.

"What this means for Laura if she were accepted is that she'd be in a normal class, whatever that signifies, with a wide range of achievements, abilities and, if I may add, 'disruptives'.

"Now I think I've talked long enough. But I want you to know that in making any decision about Laura's enrollment, I'll have to rely on her records and the recommendations of your psychologist and ours. By the way, if Laura is nine, then her normal class is the fourth grade. Is the small class size the reason that you are suggesting third grade for her?"

"That's the main reason, Dr. Lowell. The other is her level of academic achievement. I don't know where Laura stands in her reading and arithmetic, but it must be pretty low. I'd hate to see her placed in a situation where she's so far behind that she is licked before she starts. Even under ordinary circumstances this could be difficult. You see, I'm being quite realistic about the problem, and Laura's placement with younger children doesn't bother me — in fact, it might be a help, especially if there are others in the class who are also behind academically."

"I see." Dr. Lowell replied. "Tell me, what about her health, physically speaking?"

"Aside from the usual childhood diseases, Laura has been as healthy a specimen as you'll ever find. She rarely misses a day of school."

"And her intellectual ability, Mrs. Mann?"

The mother hesitated for a moment before answering. "We don't know for sure. Mr. Mann and I think it's normal, but the tests don't show it. Oh, I've had a liberal education for the past few years, Dr. Lowell! I know all about I.Q.'s, Rorschach's, Wechsler's, you name it. But I'll leave it to you and the other professionals to make the judgments. All I want is for my child to have the chance to be with normal children. Maybe she'll come out of this."

"All right, Mrs. Mann, I think we understand each other. Supposing you get in touch with the Morrow School and give them permission to send Laura's records. You should also ask your psychologist to send a resume of his findings, together with his recommendation that Laura be enrolled in the Lincoln School. Since school opens next week, these matters should be taken care of as soon as possible. Both resumés should be sent to our school psychologist, Dr. Joseph Gross. Let me see, I have his schedule somewhere. Oh yes, here it is. He's due here on September 10th. He'll call you to make an appointment for you and Laura to meet with him. When you come, be sure to drop in to see me. I'd like to say hello to Laura. Then as soon as Dr. Gross makes his recommendation, I'll get in touch with you and let you know the outcome. I'm sorry we have to delay the decision this way, but I'm sure you understand."

Mrs. Mann left after thanking Dr. Lowell for his willingness to consider her request and agreeing to get Laura's records to Lincoln School as soon as possible.

The following week school opened with the usual flurry of activities. There were new students, old students; new teachers, old teachers; new textbooks, old textbooks; new parents, old parents; new problems and old problems. After a few days when things settled down to what Dr. Lowell always referred to as a "slow boil", Dr. Gross, the school psychologist, came in to see the Principal. After exchanging the usual pleasantries, the psychologist said, "I found a couple of interesting letters when I checked in today about a girl named Laura Mann. One's from the Morrow School, and the other's from Dr. Martin Grant, a psychologist here in town. I gather you've already been involved. What's the background?"

Dr. Lowell described his meeting with Mrs. Mann, and then asked the psychologist about the reports on the girl.

"The School's report is very sketchy, but this is to be expected. After all, it's a private school and we won't get too much in writing. She's reading at the 1.8 level, and she's at the 2.1 level in arithmetic. Her attendance is excellent. And that's just about all they report. It's what they don't say that raises questions in my mind. For example, there is no I.Q. And the only information in the section titled 'anecdotal remarks' is that Dr. Grant is her psychologist. They're certainly cautious about what they put in writing.

"Dr. Grant is a bit more explicit. He's seen Laura for the past three years on a weekly basis. According to him, the girl has an I.Q. of at least 59 according to the Stanford-Binet, but this score cannot be considered to be accurate because of her emotional instability. Let's say the score is minimal. As for Laura's emotional problems, Dr. Grant states that she is schizophrenic, probably of the hebephrenic type."

"I hate to display my ignorance," Dr. Lowell interrupted, "but just what does that mean? You psychologists have a language all of your own, and no one else can understand you."

"Just like you educators with your pedagese," Dr. Gross laughingly retorted. "Anyhow, hebephrenia is characterized by silliness, delusions, hallucinations and very often, regression. Be that as it may, Dr. Grant feels that there's been a definite improvement in Laura's behavior over the past year and he would like to see her in a normal school situation. His comments suggest that Laura might not be easy to handle. But he does feel that the girl's condition might improve if she has a chance to be in a regular class and with the right teacher."

"What's the prognosis in cases such as this, Dr. Gross?"

"As a rule, poor. But there's always hope. I want to see the girl and will arrange an appointment as soon as possible. I'll also call Dr. Grant and see if there's anything more he'd like to tell me. Then I'll be in a better position to tell you what I think."

Several days later Dr. Lowell's secretary informed him that Mrs. Mann and her daughter were there and wanted to say hello. The mother came in with Laura by the hand. The girl, a bit tall for her nine years, had a wealth of short, red hair. She looked at the Principal for only a second and then her eyes darted around the office, rarely lighting for more than an instant on any one object. Her mother said to her,

"Honey, this is Dr. Lowell, the Principal of this school."

"Hi, Laura, I'm glad to meet you."

Ignoring his proferred hand, the girl looked up at her mother and said, "How come he's not a lady, like Miss Baird?"

"Well," the mother replied, "Miss Baird is the Principal of the other school. Dr. Lowell is the Principal here. Now let's go play games with the other man I told you about. Say goodbye to Dr. Lowell."

"Goodbye," the girl answered dutifully, and started to tug at her mother. "Come on, let's go. I want to play."

About an hour later Dr. Gross came into the Principal's office. He had some papers in his hands, and before he could speak, Dr. Lowell asked, with a grin on his face, "And did we play some games this morning, Dr. Gross?"

"Sure did," the psychologist grunted. "Isn't it nice to earn a living this way? All I do is play games. Want to trade jobs?"

"No thanks. Seriously, what do you think about Laura?"

Dr. Gross hesitated for a moment and then began. "This is one of those cases where you're damned if you do, and damned if you don't. We did play games, and from her drawing and the Rorschach, I am convinced that Laura is a disturbed girl. The question is, how much? And we can't be sure of that. I talked with Dr. Grant yesterday and he was quite positive about the progress Laura has made. That being true, I asked 'why not let her continue where she is now?' His answer, and I'm tempted to go along with him, is 'wouldn't she do even better in a more normal situation?' Maybe so, but no one can really predict.

"Now we could insist on a psychiatric evalution of Laura. Supposing we request that the school retain a psychiatrist to make an evaluation of Laura's condition.

By the time he makes his recommendation, another six or eight weeks will have elapsed, and what happens to Laura in the meantime? Should she enroll in the Morrow School, or wait and enter Lincoln several months late and be behind the others in class work? If my prediction is right, the psychiatric examination will also be inconclusive and we'll be weighing the same pros and cons then as we are now.

"Dr. Lowell, I would recommend that we accept Laura, providing you think we have a teacher who can give Laura the kind of attention she will need. If you have such a person, I'd be glad to work with her but you must realize I'm here only two mornings a week. And, I'm sure I don't have to remind you, I have a few other things to do besides help with Laura."

"And so does the teacher," interjected the Principal. "Then you think we should accept the child. I'd like to think about this a bit. Meanwhile, leave those reports, unless they're considered confidential. By the way, what did you tell Mrs. Mann?"

"I told her she would hear from you one way or the other, before the end of the week. As for the reports, the one from the Morrow School can be made part of Laura's record, that is, if she comes here. As for the one from Dr. Grant, I think it might be better if you mark it confidential after you've read it and let me hold on to it. See you next week, and good thinking!"

The Principal did, indeed, do some serious thinking — "soul-searching", as he often referred to the decision-making process. And his decision to accept Laura was in no small way influenced by the small class sizes, but even more important, by the availability of an excellent group of third-grade teachers. Each of the four had excellent qualities, but he was convinced that Sally Norton had just what was needed in this situation. When she came to his office the next day, he briefed her about Laura and told her of his conversation with Dr. Gross. He concluded by saying, "Sally, perhaps you're wondering why I'm asking you to take on this child. Quite simply, I think you might have a better chance of success than your collegues. Miss Scott has been with us for only one year, and although she gives every indication of being an excellent teacher, I don't think it's fair to place Laura with her at this early stage in her career. Mrs. Meyer and Mrs. Hill are going to be up to their necks in trying some team teaching, although either one of them would do a fine job with Laura. Besides, you've done outstanding work here for the past three years, and I'm convinced that if anyone will succeed with Laura, you will. I think you have the right combination of permissiveness and firmness that Laura needs. Say, why are you sitting there smiling like a Cheshire cat?"

Miss Norton burst into laughter and answered. "I was just thinking how much I'm going to enjoy that luncheon the girls are going to buy for me. You see, Dr. Lowell, we've been talking about Laura in the faculty room ever since the opening day of school. The children who live on her block have been telling us that Laura told them she would be in our third grade soon. And believe me, some of the tales we get seem to be straight out of the abnormal psychology course I took during the summer. Seriously, though, I'll do the best I can, but I'll need all the help I can get. I'm sure it won't be easy."

The Principal thanked the teacher for agreeing to take Laura, and while dialing Mrs. Mann's telephone number, muttered to himself that the neighborhood radar system hadn't lost any of its usual efficiency. When Mrs. Mann answered and learned about the decision, the mother was overjoyed, and promised the Principal her complete cooperation. He told her to bring Laura to school the following Monday and, after leaving Laura with Miss Norton, to report to his office to complete the child's registration. He suggested that Mrs. Mann bring Laura a half an hour before the opening of school in order to discuss the child with the teacher.

The following Monday, after he had obtained the usual registration information from Mrs. Mann, Dr. Lowell settled back in his chair and asked, "How did things go this morning?"

"Just fine. Laura took to Miss Norton immediately, and I can tell that they'll get along well together. I left just before the other children came in. I do so hope this will work out for Laura."

"So do I," the Principal replied. "But let's understand some of the ground rules. Miss Norton will be in touch with you about Laura's progress from now on. I won't 'get into the act', so to speak, unless it becomes necessary. That doesn't mean that Miss Norton won't keep me informed, but just that your main contact will be with her. If she's having any serious trouble, you'll hear about it soon enough. Good luck, Mrs. Mann, and let's keep our fingers crossed."

Several weeks elapsed before Dr. Lowell had the opprtunity to talk at length with Sally Norton. There always seemed to be something that had to be done — observing new teachers, attending grade conferences, District conferences, PTA conferences, as well as myriad other routine duties — which left little extra time. However, Dr. Lowell had not forgotten Laura, nor was he unaware of her presence. He saw her occasionally in the hall when her class was going to physical eduction or to music. He noticed that Laura was always at the head of the line where Sally Norton usually held her by the hand. On three occasions, Dr. Lowell dropped into Miss Norton's class for an informal observation and noted that Laura was seated near the teacher, whether the class was working in large or small groups. Also, he had been gratified to receive a note from Mrs.

Mann three weeks after Laura had entered Lincoln saying that "Laura has never seemed so happy."

Early in November, Dr. Lowell arranged for a conference with Miss Norton. He asked how Laura was getting along.

The teacher replied, "So far, so good — but, Dr. Lowell, it's not easy. The child's attention span is so limited, I've got to keep her right under my nose all the time. And she comes out with the wildest ideas, most of them completely unrelated to what's going on at the time. If I didn't know her background, I'd say she is a most uninhibited child. One example of her outspoken 'informality', you might say, is that she's taken to calling me 'Sally' lately. I suppose when you analyze it, she considers me her pal, and I should be pleased. But it hardly makes for good discipline in the class!

"Academically she's holding her own. That is to say, she's barely reading at beginning second grade level. I have three others at about the same level, so we have a nice chummy little reading group. Laura has named it the Wildcats!

"As for her arithmetic, she's able to handle concepts, but only with great difficulty. She simply can't concentrate long enough. And when she finally understands the point, she forgets it by the next day, and we have to start all over again. Did I say the next day? Depending upon her mood, it could be the next minute! Let's face it, she'll never rival Einstein!

"However, Dr. Lowell, there is one thing that's beginning to worry me, and that is Laura's relationship with the other children, or is it the other way around? I've talked this over with Dr. Gross on several occasions. You see, Laura needs constant attention — maybe the word should be 'surveillance', and the other kids are beginning to resent this. In a way they're no different than Laura. Everyone wants to be loved, and I suppose the extra attention I have to give to Laura makes her the teacher's pet in their eyes. As a result, there's a gradual but noticeable change in the class' attitude toward her. At first, they were very helpful and understanding. They'd wait their turns patiently, that is, for third graders, while I took care of Laura's needs — really, demands. Now the children are making it clear that they, too, need me. And they do, Dr. Lowell. Some days I feel like shouting 'there are so many of you and so few of me'.

"Another thing. The group's resentment is taking on other forms. I notice they don't tolerate Laura's wild statements as well. They are beginning to recognize that the child's contributions are quite far-fetched — even for this imaginative age level.

"Oh, yes, there's one more thing you should know, Dr. Lowell. My relationship with Mrs. Mann is very good. She's been in to see me several times, at my request, and she's been most cooperative. She's helping Laura at home with both reading and arithmetic. The Manns' certainly showed their pride in Laura when they attended Open School Night a few weeks ago. It was interesting to note, though, that several of the other parents asked me about Laura. It's obvious to me that it wasn't because of their sympathy for the child. I suspect their own children have told them some beauts about Laura's antics, and these parents are probably wondering how I can cope with Laura's problems and teach their darlings as well. Can't say I blame them. I'm beginning to wonder about it myself."

Dr. Lowell had listened to Sally Norton without interruption. As the teacher talked, he began to have some disquieting feelings about his decision to accept Laura. In spite of the teacher's attempt at humor, it was becoming obvious that she was controlling an explosive situation that might become serious as the school year progressed.

"You're doing a grand job, Miss Norton," he began. "There's no doubt in my mind that you're handling the situation as well as anyone could. All I can add is that if I can be of any help, please let me know, and don't hesitate to keep me informed. I'm interested in Laura, but I'm also concerned about you and the rest of the class. I know you're keeping in touch with Dr. Gross and that he's working with you. You certainly have shown patience and understanding beyond what is usually required. I certainly hope you collected that luncheon from the other teachers. You deserve it!"

It was late in January when Dr. Lowell had another conference with Sally Norton to discuss Laura. The teacher asked to see the Principal as soon as the children had left for the day. When she started to speak, she seemed agitated and nervous.

"Dr. Lowell, something happened this afternoon that I think you should know about. There might be some repercussions, and I think you should have all the facts.

"I've deliberately refrained from talking with you about Laura since I saw you last November. Everything I said about her then still holds, but I thought I would be able to handle her. Now, I'm not so sure.

"Let me back up a bit. You remember my telling you about the increasing resentment of the other children in the class towards Laura. Well, I tried to rectify that by giving them more attention. I don't neglect Laura, but on occasion I make her wait for my full attention because I am busy with others. She can't seem to tolerate this and becomes particularly annoying when I work with other groups. She constantly runs up to me and asks questions, some of them rather inane. She persists in trying to get attention, and putting her off is never easy. She was very close to a temper tantrum on at least two occasions.

"Dr. Gross has made it quite clear to me that Laura's

actions stem primarily from her lack of security, and the other children are a threat to her. I understand this, but even in a comparatively small group of 23, there's a limit to what one can do. You remember the Christmas play incident, don't you?"

"I don't think I'll ever forget it, Sally. I know it took some real planning to be sure that every kid, including Laura, had a part in the play. Casting her as an angel who had no lines to remember was a great idea, but who could predict that she would spontaneously step out to the front of the stage, wave her hand and yell, 'Hi, Mom'? Well, it brought the house down, didn't it?"

"It sure did, Dr. Lowell. It also brought the roof down over my head after we got back to the classroom. The class wasn't happy about it at all. 'She spoiled our play', many of them said. They were mad because she didn't play her part right, and probably because she upstaged them to boot. Those kids are a bunch of hams at heart.

"Thank goodness for the Christmas vacation. I was able to forget Laura and her antics for a while. But the holiday didn't change anything. We picked up right where we had left off, but with a difference. The children are now beginning to tease and torment Laura. In other words, they're beginning to strike back. As you well know, kids can be kind and considerate, but they can also be vicious and even sadistic. And, I might add, the girls are no better than the boys. I'm sure they wouldn't act like this toward Laura if she had a visible affliction, like an arm or a leg in a cast. Then they could see that something's wrong and would probably be helpful and cooperative. But they can't see what causes Laura's 'infirmity' and I don't think I should explain it to them. So, they react to her behavior. Obviously they don't like it.

"This afternoon we were all working at our desks.

The children had scissors they were using to cut out paper designs for valentines. I was in the back of the room helping one of the children when I heard a shriek. I turned, and there was Laura chasing Frankie Sommers around the room, holding the pair of scissors as if it were a knife with which she intended to stab him. She had a glint in her eye, Dr. Lowell, as if she really meant business if she caught up with him. Fortunately, I was able to grab her and hold on to her. She gave up the scissors willingly enough, but she burst into tears and kept crying, 'He keeps calling me crazy all the time! He just sits there next to me and keeps saying over and over again, just loud enough for me to hear, 'Crazy Laura, Crazy Laura, Crazy Laura'.

"You could have heard a pin drop in the room. Fortunately, it was near the end of the day, so I told the class to keep on working until time to go home, but I sat Laura next to me. I asked her and Frank to stay after school for a few minutes. The boy admitted saying what Laura claimed he had said, but insisted that Laura had been annoying him too. You know how it is, Dr. Lowell, each one claims the other one started it. I told Laura she must never try to hurt anyone again, and I sent them home after they shook hands and agreed to be friends. I'm quite certain that Laura won't say anything to her mother about this. In fact, the child has probably forgotten about it by now. But, I'm quite sure Frank's mother will hear about the incident, either from her son or from the other kids. They really were scared, you know. And to be truthful, so was I. What do you think ought to be done?"

"I appreciate your coming to me right away, Sally. I'm sure there was nothing you could do to prevent the incident, and the way you handled the whole affair was wonderful. I think I had better call Mrs. Mann and tell her about this afternoon's episode. You call Mrs. Sommers before it gets blown up even more. If she wants to pursue it any further, tell her to get in touch with me. I think you have enough on your hands without having parents to deal with too.

"I'd also suggest that the next time Laura gets out of hand, you bring her to the nurse's office and let me know what's happened. I'm not sure what we'll do with the child, but at least it will give you a breather. Let me know how you make out with Mrs. Sommers."

After the teacher left, Dr. Lowell telephoned Mrs. Mann and asked whether she had heard about the incident. The mother told him that Laura hadn't mentioned it, but one of the neighbors had called and told her that Laura attacked one of her classmates and added that it was a good thing no one got hurt.

Dr. Lowell then related what Miss Norton had told him, and concluded by saying, "Mrs. Mann, I hope you realize how serious this is. If that boy had been hurt, we'd be in real trouble, no matter what the provocation was. I must consider the well-being and the education of the others as well as what is best for Laura. I would suggest that you keep her home for a day or two and try to impress upon her the necessity of controlling herself. Perhaps you ought to take her to your psychologist, and see what he might be able to do. Please don't misunderstand me. I am not suspending Laura. But I think it might be better if she did not come to school until you're quite sure that she understands the situation."

Mrs. Mann assured the Principal that she would do everything she could.

Late the next morning Dr. Lowell sent for Miss Norton during her music period and told her about his request that Laura be kept at home temporarily. "I wondered what happened to her," the teacher commented. "It's so peaceful in the room, it's unbelievable. I did call Mrs. Sommers, and it's a good thing I did. You were quite right. Within an hour after school yester-

day, everyone on the block had heard about Frankie
being chased. In fact, the way Mrs. Sommers relates it,
'Frankie was attacked', and she checked him over
carefully to be sure there were no wounds. Anyway,
she understands the problem, but she's not happy about
it, and from what I gather, neither are a lot of other
parents. They're unhappy not only about Laura being
in the class, but also about the way they think their
children might be neglected educationally because of
her presence. I doubt whether you'll hear from Mrs.
Sommers. She's not the complaining type. But I'm not
sure how much longer we can hope to prevent an
explosion. I've got to get back to my class now. Believe
me, I'm looking forward to the rest of the day."

The Prinicipal informed Dr. Gross about the scissors
affair, and suggested that the psycholgist contact Dr.
Grant to see what he had to say. Dr. Grant agreed that
Laura seemed to be more tense and stated that her
family doctor had prescribed tranquilizers for the child
to take when needed. However, Dr. Grant expressed
confidence that the incident was not symptomatic
of any deterioration in Laura's condition. In fact, Dr.
Grant concluded, "I'm quite pleased with the progress
that Laura is making. In an illness of this type, there's
bound to be an occasional setback."

During the next few weeks Dr. Lowell's uneasy
concern about Laura intensified. On three occasions,
Laura was brought to the nurse's office by Miss Norton.
She was removed from class for a variety of reasons.
Once she had burst out singing for no apparent reason.
Another time she became so upset over a lesson on
which she was working that she tore the paper into
shreds and scattered them around the room. And the
last time, according to Miss Norton, Laura took her
books and threw them to the opposite end of the room.
In each instance, when the child was brought to the
nurse's room, she sat docilely reading, or pretending to

read a book, until her mother came to take her home. Then, after a day or two Laura reported back to her class as if nothing had happened.

Early on a March day, Dr. Lowell was informed that Laura had again been brought to the nurse's office, and that he was urgently needed there. The Principal went across the hall, and found Laura, another girl, a distraught Miss Norton and the school nurse. The latter had just finished applying a little bandage to the other girl's neck and said, "There you are, honey, I'll give you a note that you can give to your mother. Meanwhile, don't take this off until you get home." The child, red-eyed from crying, was taken back to her class by Miss Norton, who said as she left, "Miss Simms is covering my class. I'll be right back, Dr. Lowell. I'd like to talk with you."

During the interval before the teacher returned, Dr. Lowell ascertained from the nurse that the girl, Marian Hill, a classmate of Laura's, had been jabbed in the neck by a sharp pencil. "The wound was superficial, Dr. Lowell. Just enough to draw a little blood. I cleaned it out, and I'm quite certain it will be O.K. However, I think the parents ought to know about this and have it checked by their own doctor. He may want to give her a tetanus shot."

During this conversation, Laura sat looking wide-eyed at the Principal. He slowly shook his head, and walked back to his office. A moment later, Miss Norton came in and said in a resigned voice, "I think this is it."

"Tell me about it, Sally."

"I suppose you know the other girl is Marian Hill. There's been quite a feud between her and Laura. Believe it or not, I think it involves a boy. We've been doing some folk-dancing, and Bill is one of the few boys in the class who is willing to dance with Laura. Marian hasn't been happy about this — please don't ask me why. It seems too early in life to get involved in this sort of thing, but, in any event, Marian has been giving Laura a hard time. You know what I mean — little girl tricks and talk which evidently got to be too much for Laura. Instead of reacting in kind, she retaliated in her own way. I don't know what specific thing precipitated the event today. Perhaps we'll never know. I suppose it doesn't make any difference. All I do know is that Laura suddenly went after Marian with the pencil in her hand. Before I could stop her she got to Marian and jabbed her — and you know the rest.

"I think you should also know that Mrs. Hill is not a Mrs. Sommers. I've had several conferences with Mrs. Hill, and she is most unhappy about Marian's progress in school. She blames it all on Laura. 'The child's a menace', she has said on several occasions. 'How can you possibly give Marian all the attention she needs? That Laura belongs in an institution.' The pity of it, Dr. Lowell, is that Marian *is* getting all the attention she needs. To be candid, the child will never make Phi Beta Kappa. Yet Laura is being used as the scapegoat. Now, with this attack today, Mrs. Hill has enough ammunition to stir up a real hornet's nest. And she will, don't you worry."

"I think I'll go across the hall to see Laura now. I have a feeling she's probably a bit scared. So am I. Somehow, I think I failed her."

When Miss Norton left, Dr. Lowell wearily asked his secretary to put in a call for Mrs. Mann. When she was on the phone, he began, "Mrs. Mann, I'm sorry..."

DISCUSSION QUESTIONS

1. What are the standards for determining whether handicapped or atypical children should be placed in a regular class?

2. Should the school, in this instance, have insisted

on a psychiatric evaluation even though it would have taken considerable time?

3. Could Laura have been handled in a class of 26 or more?

4. What are the pros and cons of homogeneous versus heterogenous grouping of elementary school children?

5. Do you think Miss Norton was realistic about the situation she was handling?

6. Should Miss Norton have tried to explain to the class what Laura's handicap was? How could she have done this?

7. Do you think Miss Norton "failed" Laura Mann?

8. Do you think the parents of the other children had a legitimate complaint?

9. Discuss Mrs. Mann's actions in regard to Laura and her school situation.

10. Why do you think the records from the private school were so lacking in information about Laura?

11. Discuss the policies governing the confidentiality of information about students.

12. Should other school personnel have been involved in this case? If so, who?

13. Did the school have adequate psychological services?

14. What would you have said to Mrs. Mann if you were Dr. Lowell?

Selected References

The School Health Issue: Placement of the Emotionally Disturbed Child.

Cohen, Shirley: Teaching Emotionally Disturbed Children, Children, *13*: 232-236, 1966.

Goldman, William J., and May, Anne: Dynamics of Classroom Structure for Emotionally Disturbed Children, J. School Health, *37:* 200-202, 1967.

Haring, N.G., and Phillips, E.L.: *Educating Emotionally Disturbed Children*, New York, McGraw-Hill Book Co., 1962.

Morese, William C., Cutler, Richard L., and Fink, Albert H.: *Public School Classes for the Emotionally Handicapped: A Research Analysis*, Washington, D.C., National Education Association, 1964.

Radin, Sherwin S.: The Teacher and the Rehabilitation of the Emotionally Disturbed Child, J. School Health, *35:* 97-100, 1965.

Radin, Sherwin S., Cary, Gene L., Chorost, Sherwood B., Kaplan, Sandra, Garcea, Ralph A.: Orthopsychiatry and Special Services for Emotionally Disturbed Children in the Public School Setting. J. School Health, *36:* 245-248 1966.

School Mental Health Services

American Academy of Pediatrics: Report of the Committee on School Health, Evanston, Illinois, The Academy, 1966. (pp. 18-21. Assessment of Emotional Health.)

Bower, Eli, M., *et al.*: A Process for Early Identification of Emotionally Disturbed Children, Bulletin of the California State Department of Education, August, 1958. pp. 1-111.

Byrd, Oliver E.: *School Health Administration*, Philadelphia, W.B. Saunders Co., 1964. (Chapter 21. Mental Health in Schools.)

Committee on Preventive Psychiatry: *The Psychiatrist as a Consultant to the School*, Washington, D.C., The American Psychiatric Association, 1964.

Eiserer, Paul E.: The School Psychologist, Washington, D.C., The Center for Applied Research in Education, 1963.

Gray, Susan W.: *The Psychologist in the Schools*, New York, Holt Rinehart & Winston, 1963.

Joint Committee on Health Problems in Education of the National Education Association and the American Medical Association: *Mental Health and School Health Services*, Washington, D.C. and Chicago, the Associations, 1965.

Klausmeier, Herbert J. and Dresden, Katharine: *Teaching in the Elementary School*, 2nd Ed., New York, Harper & Bros., 1962.(pp. 530-32. Antisocial Children and the Emotionally Disturbed. Chapter 17. Mental Health and Discipline.)

Lambert, Nadine M.: *The Protection and Promotion of Mental Health in Schools*, Mental Health Monograph 5. Public Health Service, Bethesda, Md., National Institute of Mental Health.

Misner, Paul J., Schneider, Frederick W., and Keith, Lowell G.: *Elementary School Administration*, Columbus, Ohio, Charles E. Merrill Books, Inc., 1963. (pp. 228-229. Emotionally and Socially Maladjusted Pupils. pp. 238-239. New York's "600" Schools for Disturbed Children. pp. 241-242. Comprehensive Program at Oak Park, Ill.)

National Education Association: *What Research Says to the Teacher on Mental Health*, Washington, D.C. The Association, 1962.

Nemir, Alma: *The School Health Program*, Philadelphia, W.B. Saunders Co., 1959. (pp. 192-197. Mental Health Programs at School.)

Valett, Robert E.: *The Practice of School Psychology*, New York, John Wiley & Sons, 1963.

White, Mary Alice and Harris, Myron W.: *The School Psychologist*, New York, Harper & Row, 1961.

Wilson, Robert E.: Educational Administration, Columbus, Ohio, Charles E. Merrill Books, Inc., 1966. (pp. 592-593. Service to Pupils' Emotional Needs.)

Related Background Reading

Allinsmith, Wesley and Goethals, George W.: *The Role* of *Schools in Mental Health*, New York, Basic Books, Inc., 1962.

Association for Supervision and Curriculum Development: *Individualizing Instruction*, Washington, D.C., The Association, 1964.

Association for Supervision and Curriculum Development, *Learning and Mental Health in the Schools*, Washington, D.C., The Association, 1966.

Dunn, L.M., (Ed.): *Exceptional Children in Schools*, New York, Holt, Rinehart & Winston, 1963.

Elsbree, Willard S., McNally, Harold J. and Wynn, Richard: *Elementary Schools Administration and Supervision*, 3rd Ed., New York, American Book Co., 1967. (pp. 219-220. Emotionally Atypical).

Grieder, Calvin, Pierce, Truman M. and Rosenstengel, William E.: *Public School Administration*, 2nd Ed., New York, The Ronald Press, 1961. (Chap. 14. Special Education Programs.)

Hand, Harold C.: *Principles of Public Secondary Education*, New York, Harcourt, Brace and Co., 1958 (p. 211. Discovering Educationally Signficant Facts about Students.)

Jordan, T.E.: *The Exceptional Child*, Columbus, Ohio, Charles E. Merrill Books, Inc., 1962.

Mackie, Romaine P.: Special Education Reaches Nearly 2 Million Children, School Life, *47*: 8, 1964.

Voelkner, Paul H., *et. al.*: *The Education of Exceptional Children*, Review of Educational Research, *33*: 5-138, 1963.

Wheatley, George and Hallock, Grace: *Health Observation of School Children*, 3rd Ed., New York, McGraw-Hill Book Co., 1965. (Chap. 9. Emotionally Disturbed Children and Youth.)

Organizational References

American Medical Association, 535 North Dearborn St., Chicago, Ill. 60610.

Child Study Association of America, 132 E. 74th St., New York, N.Y., 10031.

Child Welfare League, 345 E. 45th St., New York, N.Y., 10017

Council for Exceptional Children, 1201 16th St., N.W., Washington, D.C. 20036.

National Association for Mental Health, 10 Columbus Circle, New York, N.Y., 10019.

U.S. Deparment of Health, Education and Welfare, Washington, D.C. 20025. (Childrens' Bureau, Office of Education, Public Health Service.)

11

I'm A Taxpayer*

WHO'S WHO

DR. MACRAE	*School Physician, McKinley School*
MISS BRAMWELL	*School Nurse*
KEITH FABER	*Student*
MISS PETERSON	*First-grade Teacher*
MRS. FABER	*Keith's Mother*
MISS JACKSON	*Second-grade Teacher*
MISS MILLER	*School Principal*
DR. HARPER	*Superintendent*

In spite of the recommendation of the school physician that their child be excluded from school, these parents insist on their right to keep him there.

After Dr. MacRae had completed the physical examination of the last kindergarten child he heaved a sigh of relief and turned to the school nurse. "It looks as if the McKinley School has a pretty healthy crop this fall. The Taber child bothers me though. Did you notice the peculiar way he walks? Is there anything special on his entrance form, Miss Bramwell?"

"Nothing out of the ordinary." the school nurse replied. "He has had the chicken pox and mumps, and he's had the required immunizations. The parents gave no other medical history. He's supposed to be able to engage in all physical activities."

"Well, you keep your eye on him anyhow," Dr. MacRae said, "and if anything develops, be sure to let me know."

"I'll check on him again when we give eye examinations in a couple of months," the school nurse replied.

Dr. MacRae's concern about Keith Taber did not seem warranted during the kindergarten year. Keith's teacher did comment at the end of the year that the child's coordination was not quick or accurate. But this

* Reprinted with the permission of the publisher from Hamburg, Morris: *Case Studies in Elementary School Administration*, New York, Teachers College Press, Teachers College, Columbia University, 1957.

wasn't considered especially unusual among kinder-gartener children.

About a month after school reopened in the fall, Miss Peterson, Keith's first-grade teacher, asked the school nurse if there was any further information on Keith's medical record that she should have. "I think there's something wrong with that child," she told Miss Bramwell. "I notice he falls quite easily, almost as if he has no sense of balance. He's very reluctant to par-ticipate in any of the games with the other children."

"Send him down to me at your earliest oppor-tunity," Miss Bramwell said. "Dr. MacRae remarked about him when he was examined last year. I'd like to take a good look at him."

When Keith entered the nurse's office, Miss Bramwell was quite taken aback. The boy had put on a great deal of weight and was definitely in the chubby class. His gait was halting, and it looked as if he walked mainly on his toes. Miss Peterson had good reason for her question. Miss Bramwell decided to call Mrs. Taber and ask her if she would come to school to talk about Keith.

"What's wrong with him?" Mrs. Taber asked over the telephone. "Does he have an upset stomach? I think he's fighting a cold."

"No, Mrs. Taber, it's nothing like that. I just want some information to complete our records on Keith. Could you possibly see me this afternoon?"

"Well, it isn't really very convenient for me to come," the mother replied. "As long as it isn't important, suppose we make it next Monday."

"I don't know how important it is," the school nurse said, "but Keith seems to have some trouble playing with the other children. He doesn't coordinate as well as he should. Is there any information that we should have regarding this?"

"Oh, that business," the mother replied. "There really isn't any need for me to come down and talk with you about that. We took him to our family doctor just before school reopened, and he said that Keith may have a little orthopedic trouble. We may have to get him some special shoes, but it's nothing to be concerned about. He recommends that Keith engage in all play, so don't give it another thought. And thank you for calling."

Miss Bramwell relayed this message to Miss Peterson and added, "I think this boy bears close watching, even if the family doctor says he's O.K. Let me know if you continue to have trouble."

The following week, an excited Miss Peterson led Keith into the nurse's room, and sat him down on the day bed. "May I see you out in the hall?" she asked.

Once out of the room, the teacher said, "I really think something is drastically wrong. He's fallen three times so far this morning. Each time, he couldn't get up by himself, and I had to give him some help. I wonder what's the matter with the child? Don't you think Miss Miller should know about this?"

"Yes, I do," Miss Bramwell replied. And the two of them, telling Keith to wait in the nurse's office, went to see the principal.

After they had related the story about Keith to her, the principal said, "Let's get Dr. MacRae to check him as soon as possible. Meanwhile, I think it would be better to keep Keith lying down in your office, Miss Bramwell. Will you call the doctor?"

"I think he's giving physicals in the Jefferson School, Miss Miller, but I'll see if I can get him to come sometime today."

Before Dr. MacRae was available, it was time for lunch. Rather than permit Keith to go by himself, Miss Bramwell took him home in her car. When Keith was brought into the house, the mother asked, "What's wrong? Why are you bringing Keith home?"

Miss Bramwell replied, "He seems to have difficulty in walking. He claims that nothing hurts him, but he fell three times in class this morning."

"Oh, I'm sure he's just weak from the bug he's been fighting since last week. I think if he lies down for a while, he'll be able to go back this afternoon."

Sure enough, Keith was led into the classroom that afternoon by Mrs. Taber. She departed with only a "he's all right now".

Later that afternoon, when Dr. MacRae had examined the child and had sent him back to class, he turned to Miss Bramwell and said, "Would you come with me to see Miss Miller?"

When they were seated in the principal's office, the doctor said, "I think we've got a case of muscular dystrophy here. Of course, my examination was only superficial, but the parents should be made aware of this as soon as possible. All I can do is recommend that he be examined by their own doctor. But he shows every symptom of this disease. He shouldn't be in school until a diagnosis has been made. May I have your permission to send him home?"

"Of course," Miss Miller replied. "Will you contact the parents?".

"I'll call Mrs. Taber right away," the doctor said.

When Dr. MacRae called Mrs. Taber, she said irritably, "I've explained all about this to the school nurse. However, if it'll make you feel better, I'll have Keith checked again by our family doctor. What do you suspect?"

"I'm not sure, but if you wish, you can have your family doctor call me, and I'll be glad to talk it over with him."

"That'll be fine," Mrs. Taber said. "We'll see him tonight."

Keith was absent from school the next day, but on the following day he was brought into the first grade classroom by Mrs. Taber. "We're going to get him some new shoes next week," she said to Miss Peterson. "Until he gets them, our doctor thinks it would be better if he didn't play games with the older children. Keith understands this, and I'm sure he'll give you no trouble. Maybe you can give him some extra work to do while the other children are out."

"How about lunch for Keith? He usually goes home, doesn't he?" Miss Peterson inquired.

"Oh, he'll be able to do that all right. But just to be on the safe side, I'll call for him until he gets his new shoes."

And so it was. The family doctor never called the school or Dr. MacRae. Repeated attempts by Dr. MacRae to obtain more information from the Tabers proved fruitless. In fact, Mrs. Taber even refused to give the name of the family doctor to the school physician. Keith was brought to school and called for every day by Mrs. Taber. He did appear with a new pair of shoes, but these did not seem to help him. Keith remained "chained to his desk".

In January, the boy became enuretic on occasion. He was not a discipline problem, but seemed completely withdrawn. On the occasion when he was enuretic, the children would begin to make fun of him, but this was quickly stopped by Miss Peterson. His attendance was regular, and he kept up with his schoolwork. On an individual Stanford-Binet, his IQ was rated 110. The Tabers refused to give more information regarding Keith, except to say that his orthopedic difficulty would gradually be overcome.

Keith was absent for a period of three weeks in January and February. When he reappeared, he was carried into the classroom by his mother. "He had a very bad cold," she said, "But he's over it now. The school nurse called me, and I told her he was getting along fine."

"Can't he walk?" Miss Peterson asked.

"Oh, he's a little weak, but he's able to be in school now. Just be sure to keep him busy."

Miss Peterson "kept Keith busy" for the rest of the school year. The boy continued to be carried back and forth from school by Mrs. Taber. Repeated protests by Miss Miller and Miss Peterson proved to no avail. As long as the parents permitted the child to come to school, the principal and teacher felt there was nothing more that they could do. The child, having performed first grade work satisfactorily in spite of his handicap, was promoted into the second grade.

On the first day of school the following fall, Keith, weighing over 90 pounds at the age of seven, was carried into school by Mrs. Taber. "Good morning, Miss Jackson," she said to the second-grade teacher. "I'm Mrs. Taber and this is Keith. Can you tell me where you want him to sit?"

And so began Keith's second-grade year. Miss Jackson, who had been given all the available information about the child, had still another problem, which became apparent shortly after Mrs. Taber left. Keith could not sit for any long period of time at his desk without falling off the chair. He could not get up by himself, and it was necessary for Miss Jackson and several of the larger boys in the class to get him back into his place. This happened at least three times during the morning session. When Mrs. Taber appeared at noon for her son, the teacher said, "You know, Mrs. Taber, he can't even sit at his desk. He fell several times, and I had to lift him each time. I think it would be better if he remained at home until he is feeling stronger."

"He'll be all right," Mrs. Taber replied. "I'm sorry if he gives you any trouble. He'll be better soon."

But this did not prove to be the case. And when Miss Jackson lifted him back to his seat for the fourth

14

time that afternoon, she felt as if her back had been broken. Miss Miller, whose patience was now at an end, called Mrs. Taber into her office when she came that afternoon to take the child home. "I'm going to request that you keep Keith at home until such time as you can present a written statement from your family physician indicating that Keith can remain in school. I think we've been most patient and obviously there's something wrong with the child."

Mrs. Taber's face grew quite red. "I'm a citizen and I pay taxes to educate my child. I don't see what right you have to make it impossible for him to get his education along with other children. I know he's a problem, but why should he be deprived of being with the others?"

"That's just the point, Mrs. Taber. All that I'm asking is a letter from your doctor indicating that he may attend school. I wonder if I might make this suggestion. Why don't you permit our school physician to examine him in your presence? After all, we, too, are concerned with what is best for Keith."

"That's agreeable with me," Mrs. Taber said. "I'm sure he'll find nothing wrong. When do you want to make it?"

"I'll call you to arrange a mutually agreeable appointment. Meanwhile, I'm going to insist that you keep Keith at home."

Mrs. Taber flounced out of the office, and returned two days later, with Mr. Taber as well as the child, for the physical examination. Meanwhile, with the superintendent's approval, Dr. MacRae had engaged the services of Dr. James Gover, an eminent orthopedic specialist. Keith was examined thoroughly by both physicians in the presence of his parents. Both doctors agreed, after consultation, that the child gave every evidence of having muscular dystrophy, and the parents were so informed.

In collaboration with the superintendent and Dr. MacRae, a letter was sent by Miss Miller excluding Keith from school. The letter contained an offer to provide a special teacher for the homebound to take care of Keith's education at the Board of Education's expense.

On the day following the receipt of this letter, an indignant Mr. Taber made an appointment with the superintendent of schools. "I just came from Miss Miller," the father said, "and she told me that the case regarding Keith has been settled. I want you to know, Dr. Harper, that we're not going to stand for this. I pay taxes, and my boy has a right to be in school with the other children, even if it is a little inconvenient for the teacher."

"I can understand your feelings in this matter," Dr. Harper replied, "but do you think you're acting in the best interests of your boy by forcing him to attend school? After all, I feel duty bound to adhere to the recommendation of both Dr. MacRae and Dr. Gover. They should know what is best for your child, and I'm going to abide by their decision."

"I'm not going to take this lying down," Mr. Taber said, and he stormed out of the office.

The following day a local newspaper displayed a picture of the Taber family, with a story implying that the school district was heartless and cruel for depriving Keith of his rightful education. No mention was made of the offer of a home teacher by the District.

The next morning Mr. and Mrs. Taber appeared in Miss Jackson's second-grade room with Keith in the father's arms. They deposited him at his desk; then they left without a word. Miss Jackson hurriedly sent for Miss Miller. When the principal appeared, the teacher said, "What do we do now, miss Miller?"

DISCUSSION QUESTIONS

1. What do you feel are the most important human relations aspects of this case?

2. What is the legal responsibility, and what are the legal rights of the school?

3. If you were in Miss Miller's place, how would you evaluate the school's legal and other responsibilities to: Keith; the other children in his class; the teachers; the Tabers?

4. What do you understand of the medical aspects of this case?

5. How do the various adults in the case (the Tabers, the teachers and Miss Miller) seem to react to Keith's illness?

6. What problems do Keith's needs pose for the school?

7. What solution to this situation do you think would be best for Keith?

8. Under what conditions, if any, would you feel it possible and/or desirable to keep a handicapped or a chronically ill child in a regular classroom?

9. How would you describe the role of the family doctor in this case?

10. What is your understanding of professional medical relationships, and of school medical jurisdiction, in a case of this kind?

11. Do you think there is anything that Dr. MacRae or Miss Miller could have done to establish a co-operative relationship with the Tabers' doctor? If so, what?

12. Do you think it might have been possible for anyone at the school to establish a constructive relationship with Mrs. Taber? If so, who and how?

13. What other resources might have been used by the school to help the Tabers?

14. If you were in Miss Miller's place, what would you have said to Mrs. Taber in answer to her question "...why should he (Keith) be deprived of being with the others?"

15. What possibilities of future action do Dr. Harper and Miss Miller have? What do you think they should do?

Selected References

School Health Issue: School Placement of Physically Handicapped Children.

French, Will, Hull, J. Dan and Dodds, B.L.: *American High School Administration — Policy and Practice*, Rev. Ed., New York, Rinehart & Co., 1957. (pp. 392-393. Penalties.)

Grieder, Calvin, Pierce, Truman M., and Rosenstengel, William E.: *Public School Administration*, 2nd Ed., New York, The Ronald Press, 1961. (pp. 358-359. Suspension and Expulsion).

National Committee on School Health Policies: *Suggested School Health Polices.* 4th Ed., Chicago, American Medical Association, 1966. (Chapter 5. A Health Program for the Handicapped.)

Roach, Stephen F.: *Supervision of Pupil Administration and Attendance*, Law and the School Principal, Legal Problems of Education Series, Vol. 3, National Organization on Legal Problems of Education, Cincinnati, W.H. Anderson Co., 1961. (Chapter 1.)

Waleski, Dorothy: The Physically Handicapped in the Regular Classroom, N.E.A. J., *53*: 13-16, 1964.

Wheatley, George and Hallock, Grace: *Health Observation of School Children*, 3rd Ed., New York, McGraw-Hill Book Co., 1965. (pp. 476-484. Orthopedic Defects in Children.)

Health Service Personnel
and Health Examinations

Anderson, C.E.: *School Health Practice*, 3rd Ed., St. Louis, The C.V. Mosby Co., 1964. (Chapter 10. Remedial Aspects of Health Services.)

Cauffman, Joy G., Petersen, Eleanor S., and Emrick, John A.: Medical Care of School Children: Factors Influencing Outcome of Referral from a School Health Program, Amer. J. Public Health, *57*: 60-73 1967.

Cromwell, Gertrude E.: School Nurse is Part of School Program, The Nation's Schools *59*: 63-64, 1967.

Gabrielson, Ira W., Levin, Lowell S. and Ellison, Margaret D.: Factors Affecting School Health Follow-Up, Amer. J. Public Health. *57*: 48-59 1967.

Nemir, Alma: *The School Health Program*, Philadelphia, W.B. Saunders Co., 1959. (pp. 240-241. Physician, School Nurse.)

Related Background Reading

Byrd, Oliver E.: *School Health Adiministration*, Philadelphia, W.B. Saunders Co., 1964. (Chapter 20. Special Services.)

Dunn, L.M. (Ed.): *Exceptional Children in Schools*, New York, Holt, Rinehart & Winston, Inc., 1963.

Elsbree, Willard S., McNally, Harold J. and Wynn, Richard.: *Elementary School Administration and Supervision*, 3rd Ed., New York, American Book Co., 1967. (pp. 217-219. Physically Atypical.)

French, Will, Hull, J. Dan and Dodds, B.L.: *American High School Administration — Policy and Practice*, Rev. Ed. New York, Rinehart & Co., 1957. (pp. 315-320. The High School Health Service.)

Grieder, Calvin, Pierce, Truman M. and Rosenstengel William E.: *Public School Administration*. 2nd Ed. New York, The Ronald Press, 1961. (Chapter 14. Special Education Program.)

Hand, Harold C.: *Principles of Public Secondary Education*, New York, Harcourt, Brace and Co., 1958. (p. 211. Discovering Educationally Significant Facts About Students.)

Klausmeier, Herbert J. and Dresden, Katharine: *Teaching in the Elementary School*, 2nd Ed., New York, Harper & Bros., 1962. (pp. 537-542. Orthopedic Handicaps and Chronic Illnesses).

Langton, Clair V., Allen, Ross L., and Wexler, Philip: *School Health — Organization and Services*, New York, The Ronald Press, 1961.

Mackie, Romaine P.: Special Education Reaches Nearly 2 Million Children, School Life, *47*: 8, 1964.

Mackie, Romaine P., *et al.*: What You should Know About Teaching Handicapped Children, School Management, *11*: #10, #11, #12, 1967.

Misner, Paul J., Schneider, Frederick W., and Keith, Lowell G.: *Elementary School Administration*, Columbus, Ohio, Charles E. Merrill Books, Inc., 1963. (Chap. 10. Pupils with Problems: The Maladjusted and Handicapped. pp. 304-307. Health Services.)

Voelkner, Paul H., *et al.*: *The Education of Exceptional Children*, Review of Education Research, *33*: 5-138, 1963.

Wilson, Robert E.: *Educational Administration*, Columbus, Ohio, Charles E. Merrill Books, Inc., 1966. (pp. 564-569. Special Education pp. 609-610. The Nurse.)

Organizational References

American Medical Association, 535 North Dearborn St., Chicago, Ill. 60610.

Council for Exceptional Children, 1201 Sixteenth St., N.W., Washington, D.C. 20036.

Muscular Dystrophy Association of America, Inc., 1740 Broadway, New York, N.Y. 10019.

National Society for Crippled Children and Adults, 2023 West Ogden Ave., Chicago, Ill. 60640.

U.S. Department of Health, Education and Welfare, Washington, D.C. 20025. (Children's Bureau, Office of Education, Public Health Service.)

Qualifications of School Health Personnel

12

Sex Is Here To Stay

In planning a pilot project a sixth grade teaching team considers the question: who shall teach sex education?

"As I understand it then, Dr. Wayne, I will have pretty much carte blanche in developing this family-life education program in the ten elementary schools. The chance to develop something completely new is the real challenge of this job for me."

For the past hour Dr. Edward Wayne, the Assistant Superintendent of Schools in charge of curriculum, had been talking with Miss Edith Corwin, the newly appointed Coordinator for Family-Life Education for the Jefferson Schools. He had explained to her what led up to the decision to undertake a pilot project in family-life education, described the community reactions to it and reviewed the plan which had been approved by the Board of Eudcation.

"We're pleased to have someone like you who has enthusiasm for doing something a bit different," Dr. Wayne responded. "As soon as we learned that our application for Title I funds for this project would be approved, we knew its success would depend upon finding the right person to provide leadership. We wanted someone with know-how in the area of sex education. I don't need to tell you that people with your academic preparation are hard to find, and some are not willing to undertake a pilot project with the chance that it might not be continued at the end of the three-year funding period. Everything depends upon how successful our efforts are."

"Well, I see this project as a real opportunity," Miss Corwin said, "and just the kind I was looking for. As you know, I taught in the intermediate grades for five years before I decided to specialize in family-life education. The kinds of emotional and social problems that I saw beginning to develop in some of those youngsters I taught influenced me in my choice of specialization. I'm convinced that schools must give more attention to the problems we often classify as mental health, which are reflected in some of the unfortunate statistics of illegitimate births, divorces, misuse of drugs, et cetera. And it always seemed to me that we neglect the curriculum areas that might help prevent some of the problems. Very few schools are dealing effectively with education about growth and development, human sexuality and family relationships, and yet these are topics of vital concern to everyone. I've had several offers, but I am intrigued by your school system, particularly by the team teaching approach you have been developing."

"Yes, it is an interesting approach," Dr. Wayne commented. "We've had a couple of years experience now and I think we are beginning to work out some of the difficulties. Our new superintendent convinced the Board that this approach is well worth the extra time and money that it requires. The teachers were a bit hesitant at first, but now you can feel most of them getting into the spirit of the thing, and some are very enthusiastic about it."

"I'm glad to hear you say that, because I've heard both positive and negative evaluations of the team approach. Personally, I have never worked in a team situation and I am looking forward to it with a great deal of anticipation."

"I think you'll like it. Of course, we are still experimenting, trying different team designs and a variety of grouping plans and schedules. As a matter of fact,

your participation is a first for us, since we have not
previously used any specialists from outside our own
school system. We have operated on the premise that
individual members of our faculty have enough exper-
tise in the various subject areas to give leadership to
the others who might have less experience or training.
And this has proven to be true. Family-life education,
however, is a little bit different. Not one of our teachers
has the kind of background that you do. That, plus the
difficulty we have had in convincing the community
and the Board of Education of the value of a program
like this, made us decide that it would be best for
someone from the outside to provide the leadership."

"I don't think there is any community where there
would be no controversy on a subject like this," Miss
Corwin reacted. "I was quite interested in your telling
me that the Family-life education program was actually
an issue in the last election of School Board members—
and that the 'good guys' were elected by an overwhelm-
ing majority."

"Yes, the election indicated that there was no question about the way most of our voters felt about the
project, but we may still hear from the minority who
feel the other way. Incidentally, I suspect that the issue
might be somewhat controversial among the teachers
too, although not much has been expressed by them.
It's not easy for teachers to teach subjects in which
they have had little or no preparation, especially topics
that have become somewhat emotionally charged. That
is another reason why we decided to start slowly in
the fall with a pilot project in the sixth grade in just
one of our schools. Later we'll extend it to the others.
But your job starts next month — July 5th, to be specific,
when you meet the group of teachers who have volunteered to work on the family-life curriculum guide for
our elementary schools, thanks to Title I funds. I wish
we could give you more time to do some planning of

your own, but you know how the government operates. You wonder whether you will get the grant, and then suddenly your application is approved, starting immediately. Anyway, you are fresh out of graduate school and you must have lots of ideas about curriculum development in this area. You have a copy of our project proposal and know that its main purpose is to prepare our elementary teachers to do the job in family-life education that they were always expected to do anyway. In spite of the fact that some people will say with a sneer that we are teaching sex in the schools, the material on growth and development and family relationships is not new to any curriculum. It has just been neglected or poorly handled because teachers are not sure how to go about it."

Miss Corwin smiled and said, "Your words are music to my ears. There aren't many administrators who feel the way you do, believe me. To be very candid with you, they are more apt to pussy-foot around this subject and overlook the school's inadequacies. Now this is an intelligent approach — giving teachers the kind of help they need. And I think the sixth grade is a good place to start."

"We had a lot of discussion about where to start. Some wanted to start at the kindergarten level and gradually move up; others wanted to concentrate on the high school level. We finally selected the sixth grade for the pilot project because we think it is a reasonable compromise. We've always had a little something you might call sex education in the junior and senior high schools, but it now appears that much of what is taught then is too late and needs to be considered in the upper elementary grades instead. Besides, we think an improved upper elementary school curriculum will have a favorable effect on the high school curriculum. If the program progresses the way we hope it will, you will have plenty of opportunity to

work with our high school health and physical education teachers later."

"I surely hope so," Miss Corwin said.

"O.K., Miss Corwin, good luck. You'll be learning
more about our set-up here during the six weeks this
summer when you'll be working with our curriculum
development group. Incidentally, the only teacher in the
group from the pilot sixth grade team is Mrs. Dorothy
Franklin. Fortunately, she is the team leader. I think
you will enjoy working with her, and she will be
helpful when you start working with the rest of her
group in the fall. She has been with us for over ten
years and is a fine person.

"Now be sure to call on me if I can be of help to
you during the summer. I'll be here until August anyway. And, by the way, since you are moving here, you
might want some help in finding an apartment. If
you're interested, my secretary has a list of housing
possibilities."

"Thanks, that would be helpful. I know I'll be
talking with you again soon."

The next six weeks flew by all too fast for Miss
Corwin. She and the teachers working on the family-
life curriculum guide found their task fascinating, but
not without difficulties. There were many issues which
had to be discussed at length before agreements on
objectives or subject matter content for the various
levels were reached. By the end of summer a tentative
outline for the kindergarten and grades 1 through 6 was
completed. Its first trial would be limited to the pilot
project in the sixth grade of the Marshall School.

After greeting her colleagues at the first of the three
weekly periods reserved for team planning, Mrs. Franklin said, "I know that all of you met Ethel Corwin in
a formal way at our opening faculty meeting when Dr.
Nolte presented her. We're going to have a chance to

work closely with her this year, and I want to welcome her to Marshall and to our sixth grade team. I've had the pleasure of working with Miss Corwin during the summer and I can tell you that she is a most skillful leader of the curriculum group that developed the guide we're going to try out this fall. It wasn't an easy job, and we had some pretty hot discussions at times about what should or should not be included, and how we would go about teaching family living, sex educa-tion — call it what you will. Without Miss Corwin I'm afraid it would have been an unproductive exercise, but she helped us arrive at a sequence we think might work. We started with kindergarten and build up from there. We intended to complete a kindergarten through 12 guide, but we only finished it through the sixth grade in the time we had, fortunately for us.

"In just a minute I'll ask Miss Corwin to tell you more about the project and how she plans to work with us. But first I would like to introduce each of you to her.

"This is Marjorie Lord. She has been with us since she graduated from the State Teachers College three years ago. We often refer to her as 'Junior'. She keeps us up to date on what the younger generation of teachers is thinking. Incidentally, she's a real whiz at making English grammar come to life — and that's an art!

"Then, next to her is Mrs. Ann Link. She's been at Marshall School for fifteen years. As a matter of fact her family are long time residents in this community and there's even a Link Street named after her grand-father who was a mayor of Jefferson. She knows the history of this area inside out, and whenever we need any help in developing projects involving local resources, Ann is our expert. You could hardly call her provincial, though. She has traveled all over the world and gives illustrated travel lectures to the Friends of the Library during the winter months.

"Fred Schwab over there in the comfortable chair hails from your home state. He taught mathematics in a new middle school setup for five years before he came here to participate in our team teaching program. He has three wonderful kids. The oldest is entering kindergarten this year. Incidentally, none of us thought we would have any use for modern math until Fred came along.

"Oliver Stevens completes our team. He had an NSF fellowship to finish his Master's during the summer. He protests that he was overworked in his courses, but we have a suspicion that he and his family had a ball in New York.

"Now, Miss Corwin, will you take over?"

"I would be glad to, and I want to start by telling you how much I am anticipating my work with you. Dorothy Franklin told me about some of the interesting ways you've been correlating subject areas and I know you'll have some good ideas about our pilot project in family-life education. Dorothy Franklin surely did, and I was grateful for all the practical help she offered to this newcomer.

"Before anything else, I want to say a word about terminology. The official title of our project is Family-Life Education. I understand that the newspapers have been headlining it as Sex Education, and there is really nothing wrong with that label either, except that people misinterpret it. When they hear the words sex education, they often think that it is limited to teaching about reproducton and they envision the schools teaching about sexual intercourse. Actually the scope of our curriculum is very broad, as you will see when we start exploring it. It surely is not just sex, at least, sex as most people interpret it. Some of the most important parts deal with understanding one's own sexuality and learning to interrelate with others, especially with family members. That is the reason that the title Family-Life Education has been officially adopted here.

"Now, since there are only about 15 minutes left, we won't have time today to go through the curriculum guide in any detail. But I want to give you each a copy now, and if it's agreeable with you, I'll take the remaining time to review it briefly, hitting the highlights and offering a few words of explanation. Then, when we meet again on Wednesday, we can go over it in detail and discuss it thoroughly and make modificatons. After all, our curriculum group is not infallible, and you may not agree with all of their ideas. You're the ones on the firing line and may see things in a different perspective.

"First, I should tell you that there was a lot of discussion about the amount of time to be devoted to family-life content at the sixth grade level, and there was a wide variety of opinion. However, it was finally agreed that there should be a minimum of fifteen classroom hours for the content outlined here, and of course, the time can be scheduled in any way that seems most appropriate. That's one of the joys of a team teaching situation where there is so much flexibility.

"You can see from your own copy of the guide that there are plenty of empty spaces, especially in the column titled Suggested Learning Experiences. This was intentional — to allow for your own planning as you work with the youngsters. Any ideas you can jot down in your guide will help in arriving at the final product.

"Let's look at the objectives for a minute. There are three and I'd like to read them. '(1). To develop understanding of adolescent development and changes.' Of course, this includes a review of the physical changes that are occurring to boys and girls, but more than that, to the social and emotional development that goes along with it. And you will note an emphasis on helping boys and girls understand the different growth patterns and rates of maturing of the sexes. Also, I think you'll find some interesting teaching suggestions concerning individual differences.

"'(2). To present in a straightforward manner the facts of human reproduction.' Our summer group debated this topic for a long time. Many thought it should come later. A few thought it should come earlier. Finally there was concensus that the facts of reproduction will not really be entirely new to any sixth grader. Most know how puppies and kittens are born, and some have learned about human birth from the advent of a little brother or sister. At any rate, it was decided that while the presentation of human reproduction should be simple, it should be accurate and complete and should utilize the proper anatomical and physiological terms. The concepts to be derived from this part of the teaching are listed and should help us make the learning personally meaningful and not just a recitation of structure and function.

"'(3). To encourage the development of appropriate responsibilities to selves, friends and families as a basis for the development of maturity in coping with daily living.' This can really provide a framework for the understanding of the principles of good mental health — something that everyone needs. It gives us an opportunity to discuss relationships with family members, boy friends, girl friends, teachers — everyone. And hopefully, it will help our boys and girls develop new appreciations of individual differences, better understandings of their own responsibilities in social settings and more confidence in meeting the problems of growing up.

"Personally, I think these objectives are the most important part of the material you have, although there are also some imaginative classroom activities along with some suggested visual aids. But you'll undoubtedly have lots more ideas than we were able to list here. You will note that there are few films listed in this guide. That's not because there is any lack of them, but because so few of them seemed right for our situation here. Our group screened all of them, and there is only one about which they were unanimously enthusiastic in their recommendation—the one on human reproduction. It is clear, accurate, unemotional and complete. I know you will want to view it too before you decide when and how you use it. There is also a list of pamphlets and other source materials we thought teachers might find useful, and I have copies of a few of the better ones that you can have when we adjourn today."

Dorothy Franklin interjected, "And that will be in about three minutes, I'm sorry to say. But we'll have plenty of time to get into the meat of this subject the day after tomorrow, and by that time you will have had a chance to examine the outline more carefully. Did you want to say something, Marjorie?"

"Yes," Marjorie Lord replied. "Are we planning to have the same kind of grouping for Family-Life that we usually have for our Social Studies topics? For instance, having the total group of 135 together for a general presentation, possibly with visual aids, followed by small group discussions and other activities? If so, I was wondering if it might not be best to have Miss Corwin actually present the factual material to the whole group. She is a specialist in the subject and none of us has had any experience at all."

"We had quite a discussion about that during the summer," Mrs. Franklin replied, "and most of us felt that it would be much better if we regular teachers handled this area just as we do all others. Otherwise it appears that there is something different about it. I am one who feels quite strongly about this. But we'll discuss it again at the next meeting. Oh, there's the bell now. We'll continue this discussion on Wednesday. See you then."

On Wednesday, promptly at two, the sixth grade team again gathered for a planning session with Miss Corwin. Mrs. Franklin started the discussion by saying, "I know everyone has been doing homework on family-life education because I've heard a lot of informal conversation about it. And now we have a chance to dig into the subject and get our project planning underway — after all, there are a few other curriculum areas that need attention too. The three R's, for instance! And, speaking of that, we might as well start with a question that a couple of you asked concerning the amount of time to be devoted to family-life education. Some of you seem to be a bit worried about time for other subject areas.

"The summer curriculum group recommended a minimum of 15 hours. That seems realistic in terms of our other responsibilities. If it's agreeable to you, let's plan on that 15 hour minimum. I think it will give us a good basis for making recommendations for the other schools when our pilot project is over. Let's work on that assumption, and maybe we'll want to revise the time commitment after we get into the content. What are your reactions to the material in the guide?"

Oliver Stevens began. "I think the objectives look pretty reasonable on the whole. But I was wondering where venereal disease comes into the picture. I was simply appalled when I read the statistics from a recent report of the Health Department. Do you realize that V.D. is actually on the increase, especially among teen-agers? More than that, one of the things they found out from teen-agers who finally did get treatment was that many of them didn't even know how V.D. is spread. Is there a place in this guide for the facts about V.D.?"

"Yes, those facts are staggering," Miss Corwin agreed. "We reviewed that report when the question of where to teach about V.D. arose. It was a very controversial issue. Some felt that V.D. belongs in a consideration of communicable diseases, since that's exactly what it is. They were insistent that V.D. be separate from the content on reproduction and family living, since its spread is related more to promiscuous sex behavior than to what might be considered normal, healthy relationships between people. They didn't want it in the family-life curriculum at all. What do you think about that concept, Mr. Stevens?"

"Well, I really don't know. I hadn't thought of it in that light, but wouldn't V.D. come up naturally in any consideration of the biological aspects of human reproduction? Of course, it could become a moral issue. And I suppose you can't avoid utilizing the element of fear in view of the horrible effects of V.D. Boy, I'll never forget those films they showed us in the army— I wouldn't want our kids to see those, but I would like to give them some words of caution. I guess you're right, Miss Corwin. As I think of it, maybe this ought to be tackled in the upper grades along with other diseases after the students have had a foundation for understanding it better. What do you think, Fred? You're really too young to have seen those army films."

"I've never seen those gruesome films, but if you're implying that I haven't been 'educated', you're wrong," Fred Schwab replied." I got a liberal education about V.D. from some fellows at college, and I don't think much was left out. I wonder though, if sixth grade isn't a little too soon to introduce such a topic with its moral and social overtones? I don't know how Marjorie and Ann feel about it, but I'm willing to go along with the objectives and content suggested by the curriculum group. I'm much more interested in getting into the discussion of how we are going to teach this subject matter. I'm assuming that when we get into the bio-logical part of human reproduction, we will separate the boys and girls. Personally, I would feel a lot more comfortable, and I think the kids would too."

"You certainly seem to be hitting on all the major issues that we hashed out during the summer," Miss Corwin said." We discussed the pros and cons of separating the sexes for almost two days and never did reach unanimity."

"I think it's bad enough to have to teach this sensitive stuff under any circumstances." Marjorie Lord interjected. "To be perfectly honest, I'm not going to be comfortable, no matter what, and certainly not with the boys in the room at the same time. You remember that I raised the question the other day about Miss Corwin doing the major part of the teaching. Dorothy Franklin gave her reasons for being opposed to such a plan, but I think sex education is different than mathematics, for instance, and I, for one, don't feel that I can handle it well. I can understand that Miss Corwin won't have time to give the instruction to every class when the program is extended, but it seems to me that we have enough teachers who are competent in this field who could take over part of the teaching. What about our school nurses, or our school doctor? And how about the physical education people — they all know the biological foundations, and I don't. Unless we are knowledgeable and comfortable in what we teach, we can't do a good job. The kids will sense our insecurity, I'm sure, and we could do more harm than good. I think we should consider how we can involve these specialists I mentioned."

"Marjorie, at the beginning of the summer I felt the same way you do," Mrs. Franklin explained. "I thought we could and should use Miss Corwin herself to give most of the instruction, and especially that part dealing with the reproductive system. But the more we got into a discussion of what we hope to accomplish, the more convinced I became that our family-life curriculum should not be made into an unusual subject area by utilizing personnel other than regular teachers. It would result in a different setting for the children, who may wonder why their own teachers can't deal with the everyday problems of life. And it might also inhibit the kind of open discussion our kids are accustomed to. We have to be able to handle questions and answers. We can't always tell a student to hold his question until the specialist is available. If we did that, they would surely get the idea that there is something strange and different about this subject that their own teacher can't or won't discuss. I think this is a case of the first time being the hardest for all of us because it is new, but I have no doubt that every one of us is capable of becoming not only proficient, but also comfortable."

"But that's just my point — this is different," Marjorie Lord answered. "You can't compare sex education with mathematics or English where facts are facts and where there are no moral or social implications. I never worry too much about whether parents agree or disagree with what I teach and how I teach those subjects. But supposing some parents don't agree with how I handle sex education? You remember the controversy in the community last year when the newspapers announced that our schools were planning to teach about sex. There was plenty of objection, and those parents were quite vocal about it. Now, I know that the group who want this sex education program in the school did win out by getting their Board candidates elected, but there is still plenty of opposition and it's going to be like walking a tightrope to avoid trouble. One misstep and we could be through, especially if the administration does not give us full backing. I'll go along with this if I have to, but I want to tell you that my heart isn't in it. I would feel much better if someone else did it for me."

Fred Schwab broke in. "I can see the point of our

doing the teaching ourselves in a more or less regular way — the way we always work out our team approaches by reaching a group decision on the responsibility that each one of us will assume. But I really can't see what would be wrong with having Miss Corwin, or someone else who is experienced, introduce that film you were talking about and handle the discussion of it afterward. The part about human reproduction and what it means in the development of kids' attitudes and behavior is the difficult area, and it's important to present it right. What would be the matter with approaching it that way?"

"I have no objections, if that's the decision we finally agree upon," Miss Corwin said. "I've used the film with sixth graders before, and I've had a variety of experiences in the discussion of it. But I am convinced that kids' reactions to an outsider are quite different than to their regular teachers, even if the outsider is considered to be an expert. If you are a bit uncomfortable in dealing with human sexuality, have you ever thought that maybe they are too, especially when you turn the teaching over to someone else?"

"I think Miss Corwin's right," Oliver Stevens said. "And since Dorothy Franklin has had the benefit of the summer workshop discussion and seeing all those films, perhaps our dilemma could be resolved by having Dorothy take care of the few general sessions that we schedule. She is one of our team and all the kids know her. Besides, this is the way we often function, so it's not different and won't cause any question. Then we could follow the large general sessions with smaller group discussions for which we would each take responsibility."

"I'm willing to do it," Dorothy Franklin said, "if for no other reason than to prove that any one of us could do this without feeling incompetent or uncomfortable. I'll admit, it will be new to me, and I'm not sure how well I will do, but I'm willing to try."

"That's all very well and good," Fred Schwab interjected, "but I still think it would be more effective to separate the boys and the girls. If Dorothy is willing to take on the girls, then I'll take the boys. Maybe that would help overcome Marjorie's objections. After all, this is a pilot project, and I think we should experiment in ways that apply to our situation. Maybe we won't hit the right combination the first time, but then we'll try something else. What do you think, Marjorie?"

"Well, it would certainly help me to be able to observe someone else do at least part of the teaching the first time. But I know that I'm still going to have qualms about facing my own group for discussion about sex. I suppose I would feel a little bit better if it were only girls, but I'm still worried about the possible reactions of parents. And I think Dorothy ought to talk with Dr. Nolte to be sure he understands that this subject may bring repercussions and that we'll need his administrative support as principal. It's one thing to approve of the program, as he says he does, but it is quite another to face the music when the chips are down and the fur begins to fly."

"Don't worry about that, Marjorie," Mrs. Franklin said reassuringly. "I've been at this game long enough to know how important that is, and Dr. Nolte has given us every assurance of his complete support. I have been thinking about this too, and I asked Dr. Nolte to come into one of our final planning sessions before we actually undertake the project. That way he will know exactly what we are planning to do and how we are going to go about it. He might even have a few suggestions."

Miss Corwin said, "I think all of you might be interested to know that the parental objections about which you are so apprehensive are not as likely to materialize as you may think. Most school systems that have adopted programs like this have found that it was much ado about nothing, and that even antagonistic

parents seem to be relieved that the school is helping
them in this difficult business. After all, even parents
don't find it easy to prepare their children for adulthood."

"Ann, you've been mighty quiet over there," Dorothy
Franklin said. "That's not like you. What are your
thoughts about our project?"

"I've been doing a lot of thinking about this ever
since our team was selected for this project," Ann Link
responded. "Somehow I hoped against hope that we
would not be selected for this, but I am afraid that the
time for decision has come. I've been a teacher for
fifteen years, all of which were spent in this school. As
all of you know, I've lived in this community for all
of my life, and I wouldn't dream of going any place
else. My family and I feel like a part of this town. I've
seen a lot of changes take place in our community and
also in the schools. In every instance I've learned how
to roll with the punches, and I am perfectly willing to
go along with new ideas and practices. I know times
are changing, and will keep on changing, and we can't
afford to be stagnant in our outlook and our methods.
But this is one program that I am morally convinced
should not be attempted in the schools. Heaven knows,
education of this type is badly needed. But I don't
believe it belongs in the schools. It's really the families
and the churches that should be giving sex education,
or whatever name you want to call it, because it does
involve morals, ethics and religious beliefs. And teachers
are not prepared, nor expected to deal with these. We
all have individual convictions. I'm sure not one of us
thinks alike.

"Families and churches have been accused of neglecting their responsibilities, and perhaps they have. But I
feel that they must be helped to carry out their responsibilities in this area and encouraged as much as

possible. They could do just as good a job as we could, if they really tried.

"You all know that I am not one to duck my responsibilities, but this is one time I simply cannot go along with a program. I am perfectly willing to take the chance of being accused of being insubordinate by refusing to participate, but morally I just cannot do it. I am afraid that you and Dr. Nolte will have to replace me as a member of this team. I simply cannot, in good conscience, be a part of this program, nor do I wish to become a part of it when it is taught at any other grade in our elementary schools."

There was a moment of silence before Dorothy Franklin began. "Ann,........."

DISCUSSION QUESTIONS

1. Are the terms "family-life education" and "sex education" synonymous? Which do you think is more appropriate in this case? Why?

2. Discuss the pros and cons of separating the sixth-grade boys and girls for teaching about reproduction. How about the other grade levels?

3. Do you believe that Ann Link is justified in her belief that sex education does not belong in the school?

4. Comment on the teaching about sex by such specialists as the school nurse, the school physician, and the school psychologist. How about Miss Corwin's participation in teaching?

5. Discuss the advantages and disadvantages of team teaching from an organization viewpoint.

6. Do you believe that Mrs. Franklin is a good team leader? Do the other four teachers make a good

team? Would you like to be a member of a teaching team?

7. Do you believe that federal funds should be used for a proposal such as the Family-Life project, or should it be used to strengthen more traditional education programs? Was this project planned soundly?

8. Discuss Miss Corwin's role in the project.

9. Comment on the community's possible reactions to the teaching about sex education. Should these reactions influence the teaching? Is this situation any different from changing the teaching of math from "traditional" to "modern"?

10. How is Dorothy Franklin going to handle Ann Link's objections to the sex education program? Should Dr. Nolte be involved? Edith Corwin? Dr. Wayne?

Selected References

The School Health Issue: Responsibility for Sex Education

Alden, Carl B. and Blanchard, Jane: Experiences in Giving a Course in Sex Education, J. School Health. 32:127-132, 1962.

American Association for Health, Physical Education and Recreation, Sex Education — Where, When, and How Should it be Taught? Washington, D.C., The Association.

Family-Life Education — A Cause for Action, A report of nine years of family-life education pilot and demonstration proiects, American Social Health Association, The Association, New York, N.Y., 10019.

Baruch, Dorothy: *New Ways in Sex Education*, New York, McGraw-Hill Book Co., 1959.

Brumbaugh, D.S.: Home and Family Living Through Team Teaching, J. Marraige and Family Living, 81, Feb. 1962.

Elliott, R.D. and Gamble, E.P.: Evanston, Illinois Township High School Adds to Its Program: Health Education with Team Teaching, National Association of Secondary School Principals, Bulletin, 46: 226-228, 1962.

Force, Elizabeth: Role of the School in Family Life Education, J. Marriage and Family Living, 99-101, Feb. 1964.

Hoyman, Howard S.: Basic Issues in Sex Education, J. School Health, *23*: 14, 1953.

Johnson, Warren R., and Schutt, Margaret: Sex Education Attitudes of School Administrators and School Board Members, J. School Health *36*: 64-68, 1966.

Klausmeier, Herbert J. and Dresden, Katharine: *Teaching in the Elementary School*, 2nd Ed., New York, Harper & Bros., 1962. (pp. 51-52. An Appropriate Sex Role.)

Manley, Helen: *A Curriculum Guide in Sex Education*, St. Louis, State Publishing Co., 1964.

Manley, Helen, Sex Education — Where, When and How Should it be Taught? J. School Health. *35*: 21-24, 1964.

Schima, Marilyn E.: *Starting Sex Instruction for Sixth Grade Boys*, Amer. J. Nursing, September 1962, pp. 75-76.

Sex Education in the Classroom, Grade Teacher, May-June, 1967.

Shoel, Doris R.: The School Nurse — Her Role in Sex Education, J. School Health, *36*: 200-206, 1966.

Sliepcevich, E.M.: Responsibility of the Physical Educator for Health Instruction, JOHPER, *32*: 32-33, 1961.

Smolensky, Jack and Bonvechio, L. Richard: *Principles of School Health*, Boston, D.C. Heath and Co., 1966. (pp. 32-33. Controversial Areas.)

Steinhaus, Arthur H.: Teaching the Role of Sex in Life, J. School Health, *35*: 356-362, 1965.

Wetherill, G.G.: Accepting Responsibility for Sex Education, J. School Health, *30*:107-110, 1960 and *31*: 235-239, 1961.

Wetherill, G.G.: Sex Education in the Public Schools, J. School Health, *31*: 235, 1961.

Wetherill, G.G.: Who is Responsible for Education? J. School Health, *29*: 361, 1959.

Team Teaching

Anderson, Robert H.: Team Teaching in an Elementary School, School Review, *66*: 71-84, 1960.

Anderson Robert H.: Three Examples of Team Teaching in Action, The Nation's Schools, *65*: 62-65, 1960.

Bair, Medill and Woodward, Richard G.: *Team Teaching in Action*, Boston, Houghton-Mifflin Company, 1964.

l, Hollis L., and Foshay, Arthur W.: *Education in the Elemen-
 y School*, 3rd Ed., New York, American Book Co., 1957. (Chap.
 Team Teaching.)

Clark, E.K.: Team Teaching: Threat or Promise, J. Secondary
 Education, *36*: 445-446, 1961.

Educational Research Service, *Team Teaching in Elementary Grades*,
 Washington, D.C., N.E.A., 19 pp. 1965.

Johnson, Warren R.: *Human Sex and Sex Education*, Philadelphia, Lea
 & Febiger, 1963.

Journal of School Health: *Growth Pattern and Sex Education*, Special
 Issue, May, 1967.

Wellington C. Burleigh and Wellington, Jean: *Teaching for Critical
 Thinking*, New York, McGraw-Hill Book Co., 1960. (p. 61-68. Developmental Problems.)

Organizational References

American Association for Health, Physical Education and Recreation, 1201 Sixteenth St., N.W. Washington, D.C. 20006.

American Medical Association, 535 North Dearborn St., Chicago, Ill.,
 60610.

American Social Health Association, 1740 Broadway, New York,
 N.Y., 10019.

National Association for Mental Health, 10 Columbus Circle, New
 York, N.Y., 10019.

Sex Information and Education Council of the United States, 1885
 Broadway, New York, N.Y., 10019.

U.S. Department of Health, Education and Welfare, Washington,
 D.C., 20025. (Children's Bureau, Office of Education, Public Health
 Service.)

13

Help Wanted—Female

16

A parent assisting in a school vision screening program reveals confidential information which results in a demand that all volunteers be barred from such duties.

"WELL, Miss Sullivan, it looks like you're going to be carrying the whole load this year. And our latest registration figures show that we can expect 1329 pupils." Donald Long, the Principal of the Grand Avenue School, was talking to the Public Health Nurse assigned to his school by the Health Department. "What we suspected is true — there are no nurses available, even though there is money in the Health Department budget to hire a replacement for Miss Langmuir. Dr. Peterson called me earlier this morning to say that his Department has had no luck in recruiting someone for the job, and that we'll just have to find a way to operate with you as our only nurse, without the part-time services of a new 'Miss Langmuir'. Looks like we'll have to give some thought to how we can operate shorthanded and hope that the situation doesn't last too long."

"I'm not at all surprised that we couldn't get another nurse, Mr. Long," Miss Sullivan replied. "There is a growing shortage and those nurses who are available are taking the higher paying jobs in industry. We were lucky to be able to keep Isabelle Langmuir for three years. She will be hard to replace because she did such a superb job and never counted the extra hours she spent making home visits and conferring with parents. I really don't know how we will manage without her, but one thing is certain: we simply can't provide as many services as we have in the past. Something has to give."

"Yes, I suppose so, and the question is what? We've got to continue the health examinations, though I suppose we can encourage more parents to have them done by their family physicians. In a middle class community like this, most of them can afford it. Even so, these examinations, wherever they are done, require a lot of record keeping on your part and I know that can be time consuming. We can probably shift some of the responsibility for first aid during designated periods to some of our teachers who are qualified. That might free some of your time for other duties. Beyond that, I'm not sure what we can do. You must have some ideas about how to streamline our services until we get more help. What do you see as the major immediate problems?"

"Even before school opens next month," the nurse replied, "there's plenty of work to do in connection with the entering kindergartners and other new admissions. We're getting set up for that now. We need to get health histories, make sure that the kids are properly immunized and find out about any particular health problems. The PTA helps with much of this, and I think we will be able to manage all right. Then, as soon as school opens, my first job is to get started on vision screening. And here is the rub. I just don't see how I can accomplish this all by myself."

"As I remember it, you and Miss Langmuir just barely finished the vision screening by the end of the last school year, isn't that right?" Mr. Long asked.

"Yes, it was a real problem. There are so many children to screen, now that we are checking eyes every year."

"I wonder if there is any way that we could involve the teachers in this process to expedite matters and relieve you a bit?"

"As a matter of fact, we tried that last year. We arranged for each teacher to accompany her entire class to a room adjacent to the screening room. She supervised them while Miss Langmuir and I took them one by one for screening. Then the teacher escorted them all back to their own classroom. While the teachers didn't really complain about this, I think they felt that it was a waste of their time to have to do it. And it probably is. It isn't really necessary for the whole class to have to spend over an hour away from their regular instruction. Where I really need help is in the screening process itself — especially the recording. Is there anyone who could do that for me?"

"I don't know. None of the teachers have enough unscheduled time to help you. Besides, I don't think it is right to take away the little time they have for preparation."

"It doesn't have to be a teacher. What about your secretary? Could she be assigned to this?"

"That's out of the question," the Principal replied. "If you ever spent a whole day in this office, you would get an idea of how busy Miss Smith is. She just has to be available for all of the things that come up — she has scores of interruptions daily by parents, teachers, visitors and pupils. And that telephone never seems to stop ringing. I just can't spare her."

"Well, there is one other way I can think of," Miss Sullivan said. "How about using parent volunteers? We've used them with our summer round-up program and it has been satisfactory. What would you think about using them for vision screening? I know that it is done in some schools, though not by any nearby."

"That might be a possible solution. I think we could get some volunteers from the PTA. At least, I could ask Mrs. Bolton, the President, to find out who might be interested. Then it would be up to you to train them for whatever you want them to do. How many would you need?"

"I could use two for each screening session — one to record and the other to supervise the children as they wait. Also, I think we could try bringing the children to the screening room in groups of four or five this year so that the classroom work will not be interrupted so much."

"That sounds like a good idea. So you would need two for each screening session. That's about two hours in the morning and two in the afternoon. I can ask Mrs. Bolton to have volunteers sign up for the days and times they can come, and when we get their names, you can arrange to meet with them."

"It's surely worth a try," the nurse commented. "If it works out well, perhaps we can use these same women in other ways throughout the year."

About a week after the opening of school Mr. Long dropped into Miss Sullivan's office and handed her a list of names. "Here are your helpers, Miss Sullivan. Mrs. Bolton asked for volunteers at the opening PTA executive committee meeting last night, and these eight women said they would be glad to help. Even if one or two drop out for one reason or another, I think you have enough to carry out the vision screening program on a regular schedule. I think this is a great idea. Besides helping you, I think it will be good to have parents learn at first hand more about how schools function."

"Thanks, Mr. Long. I'm pleased that so many are willing. I'll be in touch with them early next week to set up an orientation meeting and arrange for a working schedule."

The vision screening program proceeded smoothly.

Miss Sullivan was delighted with the volunteers. As she told Mr. Long, "I had one session with them when we ran through the entire procedure and discussed it thoroughly. They learned quickly and they certainly take their jobs seriously. They are really relieving me of some of the tasks that don't require a professional anyway, and they seem to love it. They are thanking me for letting them help! That's a real switch, isn't it? Why don't you drop in and see our screening program in operation this afternoon? We're in room 208."

"I sure will," Mr. Long replied. "I'll be there as soon as my one o'clock appointment leaves."

What Mr. Long observed in Room 208 later in the afternoon pleased him. Outside of the classroom there were three children waiting their turn for the vision check. One of the PTA volunteers was in charge of them, seeing that only one at a time entered the room and stood on the measured mark for viewing the Snellen chart placed on the opposite wall. She also handed the nurse a slip of paper with the name of each child for identification purposes. It all proceeded like clock-work. Miss Sullivan read off the name of the child so that the second volunteer, seated at the desk, could locate his health record. Then the nurse gave each child directions about what to do, covering one eye at a time and reading aloud the indicated line of letters. As she tested each eye, she told the recording volunteer what numbers to insert in the appropriate spaces on the child's health record. It took less than five minutes for each child.

Mr. Long commented, "You ladies are certainly doing us a fine service. I've never seen this process move so smoothly. You may not be school nurses, but no one could tell the difference!"

"Yes, aren't they wonderful?" Miss Sullivan added. "I don't know what I'd do without them."

The Principal left with a feeling of satisfaction that everything was going so well.

Early in November Miss Sullivan received a telephone call from the mother of a second grader, Janice Ward. Though not known to Miss Sullivan personally, Mrs. Ward was known by her reputation in the community. Both she and her husband were leaders in various civic endeavors and were highly respected for their efforts. After identifying herself as Janice's mother, Mrs. Ward said, "What's this I hear about my child being half blind?"

"I don't know what you mean," Miss Sullivan replied.

"Well, my next door neighbor, Mrs. James, told me this morning that a friend she met in the grocery story told her that Janice is half blind. I just want to know what this is all about."

"Mrs. Ward, I really don't know. Can you tell me who said this to your neighbor?"

"Yes, it was Jane Richlan. I understand she has been giving eye tests over at school this fall."

"Oh," Miss Sullivan reacted, "Mrs. Richlan and several other PTA volunteers have been assisting me in vision screening this year since we can't find another nurse. As for Janice, I'll be glad to look up her record and let you know the results of her eye check. Can you hold on for just a minute?"

"Yes, I can. But before you look it up, I want you to know that I am not only interested in the outcome of the screening, but I am also concerned that information like this is being made available to people like Mrs. Richlan. Frankly, I don't like the idea of my neighbor telling me that she heard from some other friend that Janice is half blind. This is none of their business."

"I couldn't agree with you more, Mrs. Ward," Miss Sullivan replied. "I'm a stickler about the confidentiality of health records, and I can't understand anyone making such statements. If it is true that Mrs. Richlan or any of the other volunteers are not observing their obligation, I will certainly do something about it. Let me check it through and I'll talk with you again."

"Please do, because I am quite upset about it. Now, I would appreciate your letting me know about Janice's test. If she is really having problems, I should think you would have notified me."

"Of course, we always do, but only after a recheck, if one is indicated. Now, let's see, here is Janice's record and I can tell you that she is marked for a recheck since she did not rate 20/40 in her left eye. We will be rescreening these youngsters again next week, and after that, you will be informed of our findings."

"For your information, Miss Sullivan, we already know about Janice's eyes. She suffers from amblyopia ex anopsia — you know, a lazy eye, and she is under professional care which will eventually correct the condition. As you well know, it is quite common."

"I'm glad to hear that you have consulted a professional, Mrs. Ward. So many parents think this condition is not serious and don't do anything about it until it is too late. I'll be in touch with you again very soon. I want to see what I can find out about what you have reported. I certainly regret it."

As she put down the telephone, Miss Sullivan wondered how she should approach the problem. Mrs. Ward was a reasonable woman, and obviously was concerned about what appeared to be a violation of confidentiality. Should she talk with Mrs. Richlan individually about this specific complaint or should she talk about the situation in a general way with all of the volunteers together? Mrs. Richlan was most generous with her time and was the only woman who devoted two full days each week to help out with the screening. She had been assigned to recording the screening results on the health record cards and did her work most efficiently. She had one child in the sixth grade and had been active in the PTA throughout the years that her boy had been in the Grand Street School.

The nurse decided to talk with Mr. Long about the situation and get his advice about the best way to handle it.

When he heard the story, Don Long said, "I was afraid this program was going almost too smoothly. And the complaint *would* have to involve Jane Richlan. She always likes to have her hand in everything around school. She means well and really does good work. She was the chairman of the Library Committee, and she is also responsible for the PTA newsletter. She has done so many things for our school that it would be hard to list them all. But she *is* a talker, and she might have made such a statement. I think the best thing to do is to have another meeting of all the volunteers stressing again the necessity for protecting the confidentiality of this information. I'll be glad to meet with you, if you wish."

"I think that would be helpful. Perhaps at the same time we might tell our volunteers of our plans to utilize their services in measuring heights and weights, and possibly in the hearing screening," Miss Sullivan said. "This would give the meeting a dual purpose so that it won't have to deal solely with the complaint against Mrs. Richlan."

"All right. Let me know when you set the meeting. I can come any day next week except Thursday. Do you think I should call Mrs. Ward and talk with her?"

"No, I don't think that will be necessary. I promised to call her again and I'll tell her how we are going to handle the situation. I hope it will be satisfactory with her. She is an intelligent woman and I am sure she has no intention of making a big issue out of this. She does have a valid complaint, and I'm glad she is the kind of person to make it directly to me."

The next day Miss Sullivan telephoned Mrs. Ward
to tell her that she and the Principal were going to
have a special meeting of volunteers to reemphasize
the necessity for keeping health information confidential, and to make sure that those helping the school
nurse understood the importance of this policy. After
she had explained this, Mrs. Ward responded. "Since I
called you yesterday I discussed this whole business
with my husband last night. We think it is deplorable
to allow parent volunteers,with no professional training,
to provide services in schools where confidential information about children they know is readily available
to them. It simply is not right and we don't think it
should be permitted."

"Mrs. Ward," the nurse responded, "you understand
that we did try to get a replacement for Miss Langmuir
and there just isn't a nurse available. If we can't use
volunteers this year when we are so short of professional nursing help, I don't think we can operate our
vision screening program. I simply can't do it alone
and teachers cannot be expected to take time from their
classroom responsibilities to help with really routine
jobs such as getting children ready for the test and
recording the results."

"If that is so," the mother replied, "I think it would
be far better to hire someone, perhaps a techician, to
do the job. And that should be someone who does not
have children in the school. We simply don't want to
have any of our children's records seen by persons
who have no right to see them. It isn't only the business
of the way Janice's eye problem was casually spread
around the community via the super-market grapevine,
but supposing there is other information that parents
might not want generally known. Why should a volunteer ever be in a position to know whether there has
been tuberculosis or mental illness or epilepsy, for instance, in a family? It isn't right."

Miss Sullivan responded, "I understand your viewpoint, Mrs. Ward. But I really think we can avoid any recurrence of the kind of problem that brought this issue to light. I'm sure that when we stress the importance of confidentiality to our volunteers, they will understand. I don't think you need to worry about another incident."

"Miss Sullivan," the mother stated firmly, "I appreciate your cooperation and your willingness to try to correct the situation, but my husband and I have decided that we cannot be satisfied as long as volunteers are being used in the school in any capacity where they can see health records. Although I haven't been active in the PTA lately, I intend to bring up this issue at the next meeting and get some clarification and some support for influencing the administration to discontinue the use of volunteers in this way. I intend to put this in writing to Mrs. Bolton and Mr. Long immediately."

When the telephone conversation was terminated, Miss Sullivan leaned back in her chair and sighed. Her first impulse was to telephone Dr. Peterson, her chief at the Health Department to apprise him of what had developed and seek his advice. On second thought she decided to delay long enough to talk with Mr. Long first. She went down the hall to Mr. Long's office, and as she was admitted, she began with a note of despair in her voice, "I think we'd better talk again about our 'Help Wanted' situation......."

DISCUSSION QUESTIONS

1. What do you think of Mr. Long's suggestions for streamlining the health services in the Grand Ave. School? Are they sound?

2. Comment on the manner in which vision screening was accomplished in the Grand Ave. School.

3. Should volunteers be permitted to assist in school vision screening? In other aspects of health services?

4. Is it feasible to make selections of volunteers for specific jobs to be done in a school? If so, what would you suggest as the criteria for the selection? Who should make the final decision concerning which parents are chosen?

5. Is there any way that this situation might have been avoided?

6. What would you suggest as school policy in regard to the use of volunteers?

7. If you were Mr. Long, what would you do now?

8. What should Dr. Peterson do when he learns about the complaint?

Selected References

The School Health Issue: The Use of Volunteers in Health Services.

Bauer, Margaret A.: Adult and Student Aides as Part of School Health Services in Secondary Schools, J. School Health, *27*: 107, 1957.

Bryn, Henry B.: Confidentiality in the Use of Health Records, J. School Health, *37*: 161-165, 1967.

Byrd, Oliver E.: *School Health Administration,* Philadelphia, W.B. Saunders Co., 1964. (Chapter 17. Vision Screening. Chapter 15. School Health Examinations (includes references to use of parents in assisting with examinations. Chapter 28. Health and the PTA.)

California School Health Assn: *The School Nurse Assistant, A Report on the Sub-professional Worker in a School Health Program,* San Francisco, Monograph #4. Oct. 1966.

Elsbree, Willard S., McNally, Harold J., Wynn, Richard: *Elementary School Administration and Supervision,* 3rd Ed., New York, American Book Co., 1967. (pp. 341-371. Objectives of School-Community Relations).

Grieder, Calvin, Pierce, Truman M., and Rosenstengel, William E.:
Public School Administration, New York, The Ronald Press, 1961.
(pp. 609-620. Participation of the Community in Educational
Affairs.)

James, Margaret T.: *School Volunteers*, New York, Public Education
Asssociation, 1961.

Trump, J. Lloyd: *Images of the Future*, Washington, National Association of Secondary School Principals, National Education
Association, 1959. (pp. 15-18. Use of Volunteers.)

Vision and Vision Screening

Anderson, C.L.: *School Health Practice*. 3rd Ed. St. Louis, The C.V.
Mosby Co., 1964. (Chapter 7. Appraisal Aspects of Health Services).

Bock, Rudolph: Amblyopia Detection in School Health Screening, J.
School Health *29*: 348, 1959.

Nemir, Alma: *The School Health Program*, Philadelphia, W.B. Saunders
Co., 1959. (Chapter 5. Health Problems of the Eyes.)

Wheatley, George and Hallock, Grace: *Health Observation of School
Children*, 3rd Ed., New York, McGraw-Hill Book Co., 1965.
(Chapter 16. Vision Screening.)

Related Background Reading

Bollenbacher, Joan: Student Records and Reports — Elementary and
Secondary, in *Encyclopedia of Educational Research*, (Ed.) Chester
W. Harris, 3rd Ed., New York, The Macmillan Co., 1960. pp.
1437-1442

Cromwell, Gertrude E.: School Nurse is Part of the School Program,
The Nation's Schools, *59*: 63-64, 1957.

Education Research Services, School Health and Nurse Services,
Education Research Services Circular, Number 6, July 1966, 40
pp. Washington, D.C., American Association of School Administrators and Research Division.

Elsbree, Willard S., McNally, Harold J., and Wynn, Richard: *Elementary School Administration and Supervision*, 3rd Ed., New York,
American Book Co., 1967. (Chapter 17. School Records.)

Garber, Anne T., School Health Record Keeping, J. School Health,
33: 125-127, 1963.

Hand, Harold C.: *Principles of Public Secondary Education*, New York,
Harcourt Brace, 1958. (pp. 114-139. Maintaining Good School
Community Relations. p. 211. Discovering Educationally Signifi-
cant Facts about Students.)

Journal of School Health, The Nurse in the School Health Program, February, 1967 (Special Issue).

Kindred, Leslie W.: *School Public Relations*, Englewood Cliffs, N.J., Prentice-Hall, Inc., 1957, Chapters 1, 2, 5.

Kleinschmidt, Earl E.: Current Problems in School Health Service, J. School Health, *32*: 222, 1962.

Mackie, Romaine P., *et al*,: What You Should Know About Teaching Handicapped Children, School Management, *11*: #10 #11, #12, 1967.

Misner, Paul J., Schneider, Frederick and Keith, Lowell G.: *Elementary School Administration*, Columbus, Ohio, Charles E. Merrill Books, 1963.(Chapter 10. Pupils with Problems: The Maladjusted and Handicapped. pp. 304-307. Health Services.)

Nemir, Alma: *The School Health Program*, Philadelphia, W.B. Saunders Co., 1959. (pp. 282-284. The Cumulative Health Record. Appendix B. School Health Records and Forms.)

Wilson, Robert E.: *Educational Administration*, Columbus, Ohio, Charles E. Merrill Books, Inc., 1966. (pp. 609-610. The Nurse.)

Wolfe, James. M and Pritham, Howard C.: Recommended Pupil-Nurse Ratios, J. School Health, *35*: 141, 1965.

Organizational References

American Foundation for the Blind, 15 W. 16th St., New York, N.Y. 10011.

American Medical Association, 535 North Dearborn St., Chicago, Ill. 60610.

American Nurses Association, 2 Park Ave. New York, N.Y., 10016.

National Congress of Parents and Teachers, 600 North Rush St. Chicago, Ill. 60611.

National League for Nursing, 10 Columbus Circle, New York, N.Y. 10019.

Natonal Society for the Prevention of Blindness, 79 Madison Ave., New York, N.Y., 10016

U.S. Department of Health, Education and Welfare, Washington, D.C., 20025. (Children's Bureau, Office of Education, Public Health Services.)

Index